Alba ad Astra

Scotland's forgotten history of space exploration

Editor
Madeleine Shepherd

www.transreal.co.uk

Alba ad Astra 2021

ISBN: 978-1-8381268-5-8

Published by

Shoreline of Infinity / The New Curiosity Shop

Edinburgh, Scotland

Layout and book design The New Curiosity Shop.

A catalogue record for this book is available from the British Library

If you enjoyed this book, find out more about what we do at

www.shorelineofinfinity.com

010621

Contents

The first edition was self-published with assistance from Bloc Press and Transreal Fiction Bookshop in 2009. *Last Man in Space?* by Andrew Wilson was published in *Fables from the Fountain*, NewCon Press, 2011. Ken MacLeod's *The Jura Recovery*, was published by Scottish Book Trust/Jura Malt Whisky Writers Residency 2011.

Introduction to Alba ad Astra Mark II

Pippa Goldschmidt

Recent and repeated 'Freedom of Information' requests to the Scottish civil service have finally unearthed copies of *Alba ad Astra*, the delay to the initial request allegedly due to the pamphlet incorrectly filed under 'sky' (perhaps a deliberate sleight of hand, perhaps an administrative error). With this – and associated information – we can now assess the importance of this pamphlet on public policy.

What is clear is that prior to the first publication of *Alba ad Astra* in 2009, the Scottish space industry was only developing in a piecemeal and haphazard fashion. Although Clyde Space was founded in 2005 and has been growing steadily ever since, there seemed little appetite for actual rocketry. Scotland's northern location makes it ideal for launching satellites into polar orbits and yet for many years neither the Westminster or Holyrood Governments appeared able or willing to devise a space launch programme that exploited this geographical advantage.

Now for the first time, we can reveal paperwork indicating that officials did carefully study *Alba ad Astra* as soon as it was published. A Government paper on assessing the potential economic impact of any future spaceport states:

> 'Prior to 2009, UK policy was perhaps overly focused on satellite capability, rather than on the means to launch those satellites from within UK territory. After the demise of the Black Arrow programme in 1971, subsequent governments diverted the limited funds at their disposal away from the French-dominated Ariane launcher programme, deeming it better value for money to simply buy a slot on a commercial launch. But the publication of the *Alba ad Astra* document (sic) has sparked a cascade of correspondence from voters around the country demanding to know why we are reliant on other (not always friendly) nation states, when in the past there were clearly attempts made at building indigenous rocket launching sites.'

A second paper, this one assessing the potential *cultural* impact of any future spaceport asserts:

> 'Scotland has its castles, its distilleries, its poetry centres. Why should we not add to this fine (and lucrative) list its spaceports?'

And finally, a recent paper examining the potential environmental impact claims:

> 'The launching of rockets off the coast in a northerly direction will do little damage to the peat

moors or machair, and likely less harm to crofting than the re-wilding programme. As *Alba ad Astra* shows, previous rocket launching sites have managed to blend in with their environment and even be mistaken for other types of activity. Whilst we do not propose to go down this route (see the recent paper on cultural impact for an assessment of the advantages to the local tourism economy of a rocket launching site), if future administrations wish to do so, *Alba ad Astra* indicates it is entirely possible for a rocket production site to be disguised and/or misidentified as a cement factory!'

Other papers show that officials made repeated trips to the sites identified in *Alba ad Astra*, where detailed measurements of wind direction and weather patterns were recorded. One local newspaper's claims of a series of illegal raves at the Kyle of Tongue – rubbished at the time – can now be explained more satisfactorily as being caused by a group of scientists and civil servants. Apparently they were documenting the extent to which loud noise might be detected in nearby settlements, and any possible damage caused by sonic booms.

Since then Sutherland has been selected as the UK's first spaceport, with its initial proposed launch in 2022. Shetland is following hot on its heels, with another proposed launch site on Unst. However it is clear that the officials wanted to secretly test the waters before Sutherland or Shetland got the go-ahead and decided their best plan was to hide in plain sight, which is why they apparently chose the vast gas terminal of Mossmorran in Fife as their launch pad. With its round the clock processing, the constant light from the flare so bright it can be seen across the water in Edinburgh, who would notice yet another disturbance here? And so the skies of Fife were lit up by the triumphant launch of the 'Sgian Dubh' rocket and the subsequent deployment of its cargo, the 'Black Watch' satellite.

With the future of the post-Brexit UK commercial space programme in question (and indeed of the UK itself) it surely makes sense for Scotland to capitalise on its natural assets, as it goes it alone. *Alba ad Astra* points the way!

Foreword –
Believable Enough

Ken MacLeod

Decades ago, somewhere in the Kyles of Bute, I came across an enormous hole in the ground adjacent to rows of new but empty wooden huts. I was told that this was a government-built site for an oil-rig construction yard that had turned out not to be necessary. It seemed a believable enough story at the time, and in a way it still does. Scotland, after all, is littered with the traces of grand projects that never came to fruition: from the Darien Scheme, through the remaining traces of Leverburgh, and the scrap metal of George Bennie's Railplane, to the local branch of the RBS, the evidence that the nation's entrepreneurial reach has often exceeded its financial grasp sprawls across the land. Quite possibly the Callanish standing stones were, in their time, envisaged as only the beginning of a far more ambitious project - some vast channelling of geomagnetic energy, perhaps, linking up with Avebury and Stonehenge and (why not?) the Pyramids (then unbuilt, but when has that ever stopped us?) to bring auroral lighting to the brochs and crannogs of our illustrious ancestors.

But after pondering Madeleine Shepherd's haunting photographs, and studying the strange but oddly compelling documentation she and her colleagues have so painstakingly collected, I find myself wondering about the real purpose of that 1970s hole in the ground. I'm not saying, of course, that the oil-rig construction yard tale was a cover-up for part of Scotland's long-lost space programme - only that it could have been, and that in this obscurely-ruled nation whose map includes so many swathes that might as well be labelled 'Here be dragons' or 'Area 51' (what *is* going on in the mountains between Loch Carron and Kintail? Has anyone *been* there recently?) the speculation is not absurd.

The reader, the viewer, must make up their own mind.

There can be no doubt, however, that the evidence assembled here will re-open many questions we had thought were closed or, indeed, never thought to ask. One that strikes me as most urgent is this: What, in this official 'Year of Homecoming', is being done to prepare the nation - and the world - for the possibility of a most unexpected return?

(2009)

Note added in 2021.

I've left the above introduction as I wrote it in 2009. Pippa Goldschmidt's new introduction brings the story of *Alba ad Astra* up to date.

However, a few additions to mine are necessary. The 'return' looked forward to now seems – from Andrew J. Wilson's subsequent research, and perhaps from the rumour or tall tale I heard a year or two later on Jura – to have already taken place. And some of my allusions above may be a little obscure, particularly to non-Scottish readers.

The 'enormous hole in the ground' I vaguely remembered from teenage holidays is now the delightful spa and marina at Portavadie, a fine example of repurposing an abandoned site of heavy industry for the leisure industry. Leverburgh is a thriving village on the Isle of Harris, but of Lord Leverhulme's grand scheme to turn it into a major fishing port and processing centre little remains. The mountains between Loch Carron and Kintail may not be quite as unvisited as my introduction flippantly suggests, but the region is certainly remote enough for major clandestine activities to pass unnoticed. Even the more populated area to the north of Loch Carron has its secrets. I myself have heard UFO accounts from the Kishorn Glen that would make the hairs on the back of any sceptic's neck stand up ... but I've already said too much.

The Last Man in Space

Madeleine Shepherd

Like all photographers, I specialise – in botany, still life and abstract macro work – but we all make images outside our usual range. We capture interesting things that come our way, beautiful lighting or curious compositions: photographs we take on impulse because a moment presents itself. Every so often, I like to sift through those images and see what gems are hidden there, what themes emerge from their juxtaposition.

During one such exercise, a group of photographs began to suggest to me that part of Scotland's technological heritage had been overlooked. Bringing these images together for the first time, making connections between disparate artefacts and derelict sites, it seemed that I had stumbled upon the remnants of a Scottish space programme.

I looked at Chancelot Mill, that big white facade which dominates so many views of Leith and Newhaven. Do you really need that kind of space to mill flour? Sure, that's what they do there now, but what if it had originally been a vehicle assembly building for rockets? Didn't these grain silos look like fuel storage tanks? This was just a one-off whim, but the next print was an ambiguous pile of circular objects in central Edinburgh that resembled the sections of a space station. Then, up on the North East coast, near Dounreay, I found the rusting remains of what might have been a previous generation's attempt at suborbital flight.

I distracted myself from this notion by turning to photos from a natural history expedition to the Bass Rock. Among the gannets and puffins was one blurry shot, looking back to the coast, of an abandoned listening station near Tantallon, only visible from offshore. Listening for what? Was it really abandoned as early as they say? This was scant evidence of such ambitious work. Maybe there was nothing in it, but the idea kept rolling around my head.

An unguarded moment in the pub found me discussing these ideas with some female friends. Most thought I was kidding around – pubs are good for that – but one took me aside and warned me that I was showing signs of the kind of paranoid delusions that eventually destroyed my mother. I huffed and puffed in disagreement, and the conversation shifted topic. I tried to stop thinking about it.

A couple of days later, another of those friends told me that her boyfriend had an interesting snippet of information to add. He worked at the Scottish Executive and was struck by the coincidence of my musings and a Freedom of Information request he'd been processing. Apparently, someone had been asking for documents relating to space research in Scotland during the 1960s. Of course, there was nothing the Executive could tell this person that would satisfy him and the man had become rather a pest. The boyfriend said that he would see if he could give me a name at least. Maybe there was something more here, but two nutters with the same delusion don't make something true, of course.

A name was eventually transmitted: Hector MacKraken. I was told that he claimed his father had been part of some kind of space research and had gone missing in Hector's early years. He thought the government ought to be able to tell him what had happened to his dad. Fortunately for the Executive, Hector no longer lived in Scotland, so most of his pestering came by e-mail from Athens. I tried to dig up what I could on the MacKraken family before seeking out Hector. His father was one William MacKraken, who had indeed been reported missing in the 1960s. There was not much else to go on, so I had to find Hector.

The name MacKraken is not exactly common in Greece, so tracing Hector was relatively simple. Finding an excuse to visit Greece was also quite easy: forests all over the country had been devastated by fire two years previously, and even the capital city had been threatened. I was to record the regeneration of specific areas for a researcher at the Royal Botanic Garden Edinburgh.

So I met with Hector in a café near Monastiraki, in the shadow of the Acropolis. I recognised him from the photo he'd e-mailed, but his wiry grey hair was longer now, making more of a frame for his long, sallow face. He told me a wild tale of speculation.

Hector barely remembered his father and his ideas came mostly from the various fates his mother imagined for her husband, Bill. She claimed his job in the oil industry was a front for a secret government project which had gone wrong and resulted in his death. She had many notions of what that might be, and Hector, applying his own kind of logic, had decided space research was the most likely one. He believed that Bill had been training to be the UK's first astronaut and that something had indeed gone wrong close to blast off. However, because Bill's body had never been recovered, Hector still hoped that his father might be alive somewhere and that the truth might lie in a box of papers somewhere in the Scottish Executive.

I wondered if this was just a sad case of a boy missing his father – but not out loud. Hector was in full flow, and drawn in by the intensity of his pale blue eyes, I was rather carried along by his wave of enthusiasm. The iced coffees were finished, and as he continued to expound his governmental cover-up theory, we set out for a wander round the stalls in the nearby flea market. Next day, I completed my official task and flew home, pondering Hector's story.

Back in Edinburgh, I realised that, if any of this was true, the government wasn't going to be much help. I needed to find another way into the story. Maybe some early research papers had been published before things became contentious?

Online library catalogues are a fantastic resource, but they can also be a terrible plughole down which the hours can vanish – it depends how you use them. This time, it was more like Alice's rabbit hole and I disappeared inside as well. At the other end of the burrow, I found a run of newsletters called Rocketry Scotland. Many of the issues recorded failed attempts at launching fanciful rocket designs: explosions in the Campsie Fells, inter-island postal services in the Hebrides and the efforts of some well-financed East Lothian amateur rocketeers were among the early accounts.

More significantly, I unearthed a couple of boxes of uncatalogued ephemera in the National Library of Scotland and a proposal by Tweedbrooke Associates for a Scottish pavilion at Expo 67. The cartons contained sketches, plans, and samples of souvenirs, fabric swatches and display items. There were suggestions for musical and poetic commissions from Alexander

Turnbull and Edwin Morgan, artist's impressions of deep space, drawings of rockets bearing the Saltire as well as the Union Flag, and draft copy for a souvenir booklet. The exhibit was never fully commissioned – apparently for being too extravagant and too divisive in having only one of the four British nations represented. Work on the combined UK pavilion went to a different company. Tweedbrooke closed down some fifteen years later, leaving its archive to the library, untouched for another quarter of a century. The unused title was Alba ad Astra.

I thought long and hard about telling Hector about my finds. I wondered if it might just be more fuel for his fantasies, but the evidence was beginning to look more concrete – and if there was something to all this, then he really ought to know. I lingered over the decision for some time and another field trip to the forest regeneration sites eventually came up. Since I was heading back to Greece anyway, I called him and we arranged to meet on my last afternoon in Athens.

This time, he met me at Kerameikos Metro Station, all excited and eager to show me his discovery! We didn't stop for coffee as he dragged me through the lanes to an antique shop by the flea market.

"Look at that! I saw it on my way to meet you!" he shouted, pointing at the window display. "It's my dad's training helmet!" I gave him a hard look and he saw I didn't believe him. "Well, maybe it isn't actually his – but it's just like the one I used to play with as a kid. Mum told me it had been my dad's," he explained. "I don't know what happened to it after I went to uni."

We went into the shop for a closer look. There was a name in Cyrillic painted on the back of the helmet. Hector dismissed that: "A secondary use. The Russians bought up surplus where they could, you know…"

Despite the 3000-euro price tag, he took the helmet off the stand, put it on and started imagining his dad's experiences. A minute later, we were asked to buy it or leave. We had to go. A walk round the market calmed Hector down and we headed off for some iced coffee. The news of my discoveries seemed distant compared to the immediacy of the connection he had just made with his childhood. However, he decided on the basis of my research that it was high time to return to the homeland.

With Hector back in Scotland, I found myself being drawn into his world more and more. I showed him Chancelot Mill and the sites of the other photos that had made me take an interest in his story. We both made forays into the National Library's collections. Sometimes it seemed we were being helped by a singularly mischievous library angel.

Following leads in the Expo 67 proposal, I looked up their holdings on Edwin Morgan. I found that the Morgan Archive was now in the Scottish Poetry Library. My initial enquiries were dealt with by an exceptionally enthusiastic woman who really got on hooked on the idea. I e-mailed asking for access to search for unpublished works and notes by Morgan. Every few days, I'd get a reply with a scan of something attached and a note saying, "I expect this is what you're after." Nothing was quite like what might have been commissioned, and since the pavilion was never built, the poem may not have been begun. It did strike me that the initial approach might have coincided with a new direction in Morgan's work.

Back in the NLS, I realised Boosey & Hawkes must have thought Alexander Turnbull one the truly great composers, or a cash cow at least! They published over 200 of his pieces for different kinds of ensembles. As well as the finished publications, there was a box of proofs and annotated papers. I pounced on this, and after some careful rummaging, unearthed a notebook of sketches for compositions, some of which were never commissioned. There was one telling double-page spread: several themes based on three As, a G and an E; ascending arrangements of As with "Scotland rising to the stars" written underneath; big chords built round G and E labelled "Golden Eagle soars"; and then some other letters, as though he was struggling to make something from W, M, A, M, L and S. The six letters looked strange to me in a musical context. Slowly the light dawned – the astronauts named in the Expo 67 box were William MacKraken, Archibald McLeod and Lachlan Smart! Not promising musical material... Turnbull was probably pleased the pavilion and its attendant music never reached fruition.

Hector had been looking in more detail at the old journals in the NLS. He took a particular interest in tracing the development of Rocketry Scotland. This began as a young boy's fantasy project, influenced by reading Jules Verne and watching Saturday-morning movie serials. As time passed, the issues evolved from hand-drawn comic books into reports on more serious projects, and finally, the newsletter became a semi-academic journal still managed by the same man, Thomas P. Campbell – a name which was to become more significant than we could imagine at the time.

Some of the later articles gave details of experiments deep in the Scottish countryside, so we decided to take a look at the sites. Obviously, I took photographs if this wasn't too risky – although derelict, some places still bore vestiges of what looked like government security. Given what happened over the following months, I won't reveal the locations, but you'll find images of abandoned structures and debris in the attached portfolio that are entirely consistent with mid-twentieth-century experimental rockets. This was interesting and hinted that serious work had indeed been undertaken, but it told us nothing of the fate of

Hector's father.

Bill MacKraken's occupation had always been stated as "civil servant"; he was a servant of the Crown and a signatory to the Official Secrets Act. If he had met his end in some government-backed engineering folly, as Hector feared, then a direct approach was doomed. The Freedom of Information Act had already failed to produce any further information and the ranks had closed against him. We decided to look at what remained of the UK's space research. Insignificant details might take on a new meaning from our angle.

The Blue Streak F13, the demilitarised British missile which was used as part of the Europa III satellite launcher, is displayed in the National Museum of Flight, just east of Edinburgh. We set out one Sunday on a three-bus journey to visit it. The site is an ex-military airfield with massive hangars that once housed airships and a WWII Mosquito squadron. If you can tuck away a space rocket, then that's what they'd done to Blue Streak F13. This unused launcher was kept company in a corner of one of these hangars by a mock-up nose-cone of the Europa system.

Hector tried interrogating the staff about the Buzzard, the UK's above-top-secret response to Hitler's V-weapons. However, his line of questioning – and its intensity – was beyond the experience of the staff. Professional to the last, they steered Hector out of the hangar and into the café. I was taken aside and politely asked about his mental stability. I made some reassuring but non-committal comments about helping him to connect with his past as part of his return – to society, they assumed. We were left alone.

Between the hangars, we could see lots of rusting pipes emerging from the ground, raised platforms grassed over by earth and small concrete structures. Of course, we attributed these to the airfield's previous use, but such things were not inconsistent with the possibility that this had been an early test range.

The next day, an e-mail from Hector brought startling news. Unknown to me, he had recently started blogging about his father's disappearance. In the first couple of weeks, things were fairly quiet, so he had decided there was little point telling me about it. Then his posts began to attract some attention. Another blogger had discovered Hector, and the cascade of referrals eventually reached some high-traffic blogs like Boing Boing and Jack of Kent. Every kind of comment, from the ravings of wild conspiracy theorists to the inflammatory posts of some particularly nasty trolls, appeared under Hector's posts, but there was nothing useful until Hector got home from his visit to the Blue Streak and found that a thick envelope had been put through his letterbox and an intriguing e-mail had landed in his inbox. The son of a deceased civil servant had seen Hector's blog and made contact. It's still unclear how he found Hector's home address, but we believe he may be a Foreign Office employee with access to details of returning ex-pats.

Hector got extremely excited when he told me about the content of the communication, adding all sorts of speculation, but it boiled down to this: the civil servant's father knew Bill MacKraken. They had worked on a secret semi-military project involving heavy engineering and fuel transport problems. The memos hinted at a large rocketry research programme, but in grand Whitehall style, nothing was made explicit. The documents also hinted at some political reasons for cancelling the project. The civil servant's father was a telemetry expert and latterly worked at a listening station, now supposedly decommissioned. I say "supposedly" because the e-mailer told us that he visits the station from time to time, and in the last month, it had started picking up unexpected transmissions. Transcripts of some of these documents follow.

However, the real clincher was that an engineer was named in one memo, Thomas P. Campbell, whose publications we'd already discovered in the NLS. It goes without saying that Hector had no doubt that this signal was coming from his father's craft. I tried to get him to consider other options, from atmospheric discharge creating the signals to the mysterious informant being a particularly sophisticated prankster. Hector would have none of it. He declared he was destined to find his father. I left him alone to calm down, perhaps for too long. I didn't hear from Hector for several months.

As ever, I had many projects on the go and had to turn some of them into a living wage. I hadn't forgotten him, of course. And sometimes I was forcibly reminded of his theories. When I was in London, I spotted a geodesic dome filled with inflatables that people could crawl into in order to experience a kind of floating simulation of zero gravity. It was just like one described in the Expo 67 proposal, although built using modern materials. I wondered if the same designer had carried this idea from company to company until someone picked it up.

Participating in and documenting Hector's quest was no longer in my diary, and I didn't really miss it. I think he felt betrayed by my sceptical attitude to what he saw as the most promising evidence to date. When a cutting from the East Lothian Courier appeared in my mail in April, along with a note from Hector about his forthcoming book, My Dad's Still Out There, I was stunned. He was asking permission to use my photographs in a hastily conceived book of shock revelations based on the mystery memoranda. His excuse for not asking me first was that I'd try to talk him out of it. He was probably right. He had included the interview cutting to show that some people were taking him seriously at last.

What was I to do? I was truly torn between ignoring this note, writing off the photos and severing all contact, or jumping back into his paranoid world of intrigue. If I did the former, he'd probably use my name on the photos and I'd be dragged into it anyway. I decided it was better to have some control and made up my mind to phone him as soon as possible – but then I kept putting it off.

Today I received my weekly e-mail from Roberta McNaughtan, an astronomer pal based in Australia. Her usual chatty stuff about possums spoiling the observations by eating the cabling was missing. Over the years, I had told her about Hector and his notions, and this week she had something all too relevant to tell me.

Roberta's job is to spot and track near-Earth objects such as asteroids, old satellites and junk that might pose a problem on entry or re-entry to the atmosphere. The orbit calculations for one of these small objects had recently come back showing a very eccentric ellipse coming in from beyond Pluto and passing very close to the Earth. The thing was definitely going to miss us, but she'd recorded some extremely strange readings. The peculiar telemetry was being decoded as she was writing, but worse than that, it seemed the object had changed its course in a very unnatural manner. Nothing like this had ever been seen in her years of tracking inert space junk. If she didn't know better, she said, she'd think it had deliberately corrected its trajectory to collide with earth, probably landing in the North Atlantic on 30 November 2009.

I still haven't contacted Hector, but I really think I should – I wouldn't want him to miss out on St Andrew's Day…

28 May 2009

PHOTOGRAPHIC PLATES
ALBA AD ASTRA

by Madeleine Shepherd
with notes by
Andrew J. Wilson

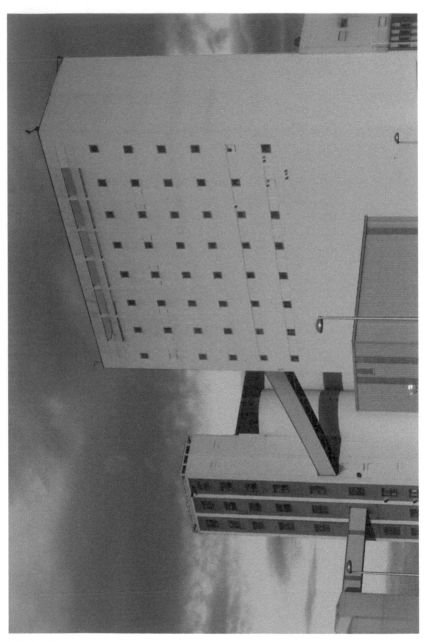

Plate 1

1. Chancelot Mill, Western Harbour, Leith Docks, Edinburgh: the second-largest flour mill in Europe. Alleged by some sources to have originally been a clandestine vehicle assembly building. "Aye, it's a mill the now, right enough," say local residents. "But back in the day, we was kept up half the night when they moved whatever they put thegither inside the place to they massive transporter ships that only docked after dark."

Plate 2

2. The "blue cotton reels", Edinburgh. This unidentified addition to the built environment bears some resemblance to a modern listening array. The Scottish Government refuses to comment on the structure, and no Planning and Building Standards record can be found. Could it represent a new generation of early-warning surveillance system and if so, what precisely is it intended to detect?

Plate 3

3. The "ploughshared" fuselage of a Z-1 "Buzzard" flying bomb found on a farm near the Dounreay Nuclear Power Development Establishment, Caithness. During WWII, the government devised a fall-back strategy that was to be implemented if the Nazis' planned invasion of England succeeded: a new front was to be established along the border with Scotland. The military's top-secret missile programme, spearheaded by many conscripted Scottish rocketry enthusiasts, was intended to form the last line of defence – or attack – in such an extremity. This so-called fuel tank is still slightly radioactive.

Plate 4

4. High-altitude pressure helmet with electrically heated visor displayed in an Athens antique shop. Hector MacKraken claims, "My father wore this in training, or one very much like it."

In fact, Cyrillic script on the helmet suggests that it was used by a Russian pilot. MacKraken's assertion that the USSR acquired such equipment as military surplus during the Cold War can be discounted outright, but it is possible that the helmet might have been adapted from stolen designs.

The question of whether the Soviets or the Scots appropriated the plans remains moot.

Plate 5

5. Closed hangar at the National Museum of Flight, East Fortune, East Lothian. The airfield was established as a Royal Navy Air Station for fighters and airships in 1915, and later became RAF East Fortune, serving first as a training establishment and then as the base for a Mosquito squadron in WWII. Although officially closed between 1947 and 1950 civil service records indicate that Bill MacKraken was posted here in the 1950s. Since the foundation of what was originally the Scottish Museum of Flight in 1975, many aircraft and aerospace-related artefacts have been acquired, including the Alpha Alpha Concorde, but like all such depositories, by no means all of the holdings are on public display.

by kind permission of National Museums Scotland

Plate 6

6. The Blue Streak F13 rocket exhibited in the National Museum of Flight. Originally designed as a British ballistic missile in 1955, the military project was cancelled five years later, but the prototype was retooled to be the first stage of a satellite launch vehicle and tested at the Woomera proving ground in Australia. Unreliability led to its ultimate cancellation in 1972. "The English Blue Streak uses liquid oxygen and kerosene as propellants, but it's a dead end," comments Lachlan Smart in his journals. "We Scots know the way onwards and upwards must be nuclear..."

by kind permission of National Museums Scotland

Plate 7

7. Aeronautical fragment held at the National Museum of Flight. This matches an illustrated description published in a 1937 Rocketry Scotland newsletter of a homemade manifold that was used by amateur enthusiasts during trials in the Campsie Fells. The outbreak of war saw the end of such attempts to emulate Robert Goddard, but many of those who sacrificed so much of their spare time and disposable income would find themselves called up to serve their country by working on the military applications of their hobby.

by kind permission of National Museums Scotland

Plate 8

8. The abandoned shell of New St Andrew's House, Edinburgh, the former home of the then Scottish Office from 1975 until 1999. Persistent rumours suggest that a great deal of the documentation that could have thrown some light on the matters explored by the Alba ad Astra project was destroyed when the building was closed. Official statements on the matter cite the problem of asbestos contamination, which is common to the Brutalist architecture of the period, but other sources suggest that the material was stored in a underground shelter located beneath the basement levels: "They had a blast-proof nuclear bunker down there, didn't they?" alleges a demolition worker who wishes to remain anonymous. "All those places did, mind. But they stored some pretty funny things under the ground, and in the end, the concrete was supposed to keep any blast contained – not keep it out, ken?"

Plate 9

9. Mothballed installation near the Chapelcross Magnox nuclear power plant, Annan, Dumfries and Galloway. Officially, the primary purpose of Chapelcross was to produce weapons-grade plutonium for the British nuclear weapons programme while also generating power for the National Grid. In his unpublished manuscript, My Dad's Still Out There, Hector MacKraken argues that the reactor was also the source of the fuel rods used in Golden Eagle.

Plate

Plate 10

10. The shell of Lord Strathbungo's Improved Skyrocket Manufactory in Angus. Strathbungo was a polymath and entrepreneur who became an enthusiastic student of the pioneering work of Konstantin Tsiolkovsky and Hermann Oberth in the 1920s. He envisaged a multitude of both commercial and experimental applications for rocketry, but died along with a number of his staff in an accident involving concentrated nitric acid that occurred at the time of the Wall Street Crash. His papers were left to the Scottish Rocketry Society, but were confiscated by the Crown.

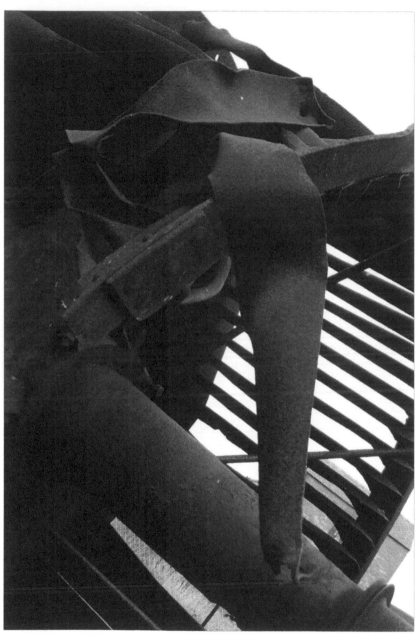

Plate 11

11. The remains of an unidentified rotary engine near Fairlie, Ayrshire. "My cousin was a trawlerman," says the farmer who owns the land where the turbine is kept. "In the '70s, the net snagged off Beaufort's Dyke. The fool dragged this thing up to the surface thinking he'd salvaged something valuable. It ruined the net and it ruined him. It's worthless junk." Beaufort's Dyke is a deep submarine trench off the south-west coast of Scotland that was used as Britain's largest offshore dumping ground for conventional and chemical munitions until the practice was officially ended in 1976. In 1997, the Government admitted that "low level" radioactive waste had also been disposed of at the site in the 1950s.

Plate 12

12. A master control recently auctioned on eBay by an anonymous party. The seller's description reads: "This is a bit of kit from the floating launch pad used for the Golden Eagle blast-off that went wrong. It's The STOP Button That Didn't Go. What's it worth to you?"

Plate 13

13. The Weightless Space Bouncy Bubble Capsule – one of the ideas suggested in the rejected Expo 67 proposal – finally sees completion on London's South Bank. "It's not like being in space at all," Hector MacKraken says. "It's not the same as floating in an endless void – and you can go home any time you like." There is no evidence that Tweedbrooke Associates were ever credited or even paid for this implementation of their original concept.

Plate 14

14. The Zeroth Institute, Cumbernauld. Calculations made on a pro bono basis by the telemetrists and mathematicians of this independent scientific foundation have determined that, if the purported nuclear engine of Golden Eagle suffered a runaway chain reaction during the launch, then it would not only have left Earth's orbit, but continued on a parabolic course that would have taken it beyond the orbit of Uranus and through the Oort Cloud at the edge of the solar system. "At sufficient velocities," the Zeroth report states, "interplanetary dust and ice crystals scooped up by the propulsion system's air vents would act as a perfectly adequate reaction mass." Working hypothetically on a number of assumptions that were suggested by the Alba ad Astra team, the authorities of the Institute predict that the spacecraft will return to Earth almost exactly forty-three years after its departure. In the circumstances, one would assume that Bill MacKraken's remains will finally be cremated when Golden Eagle inevitably burns up in the Earth's atmosphere, but recent reports suggest that the craft has been firing its retro-rockets to initiate course corrections and de-celeration procedures. Of course, there can be no possibility that the astronaut is still alive, but as Hector MacKraken asks: "If my dad isn't at the controls, then who or what is?"

Plates 15a &b

15 *a & b* Gin Head radar and listening station, Tantallon, East Lothian. Two views taken in 2006 and 2019. Built during the Second World War, this abandoned RAF base was once only visible from the River Forth, but can now be seen from the ruins of Tantallon Castle. Although supposedly decommissioned in the 1960s, it has been claimed by anonymous sources that, until relatively recently, the equipment was maintained and monitored on a semi-regular basis. The question of what this alleged clandestine activity was meant to achieve has not yet been resolved, and in all probability, never will be.

Gin Head has been stripped of all its contents, and is currently for sale for £2.5 million. Planning permission has been granted to convert the building into a private home. The estate agent handling the property describes it as "the perfect 'evil lair' if ever we saw one".

Plate 16

16 Leith, Edinburgh.

Thought to be the maquette for Sir Edwardo Paolozzi's *Ghost of a Chance*, a project that he never completed. The outline of the sculpture suggests the splitting of an atom during a nuclear fission reaction. Paolozzi was once credited as the "Aeronautics Adviser" to *New Worlds* magazine, and anecdotal evidence indicates that he also referred to this proposed artwork as *Monument to the Unknown Astronaut* and *The Kraken Wakes* at different times. The maquette is now part of a private collection.

Plates 17a & b

17 *a & b* The Zeroth Institute, Cumbernauld (see also Plate 14).

Two views of the demolition of the building in 2015. The foundation declared bankruptcy after its attempts to manipulate international financial markets were exposed by a whistle-blower. The computer algorithms that its programmers created were held partly responsible for the financial crash of 2008. It is unclear who might have written "CALL ME" on the wall shown in the second image. It is also not known who was being asked to make contact. The final statement made on the now-defunct Zeroth Institute website was "Omnia exeunt mysterium,,,", a medieval maxim meaning "everything ends in mystery".

Plate 18

18 Fountain Brewery, Fountainbridge, Edinburgh.

This facility was operated by Scottish & Newcastle until 2004. Officially, the brewery was closed as part of a corporate restructure, but a question mark hangs over this version of events. Former employees have claimed that some buildings in the complex were restricted areas that had nothing to do with manufacturing beer: "There was one bit of the site that was top secret. It had what looked like four rocket motors on the roof, and a smokestack that never smoked. If you ask me, that so-called chimney looked more like a ballistic missile. No one ever found out what was going on in there, and it was the first part of the brewery to be decommissioned."

Plate 19

19 South Uist, Outer Hebrides.

Service structure at the Hebrides Guided Missile Range. Such gantries were used to launch: Blue Streak intermediate-range ballistic missiles; Black Knight and Black Arrow rockets; and according to some sources, the manned *Golden Eagle* nuclear space vehicle. The parabolic antennae are, in fact, radar dishes.

Plate 20

Plate 20

Unknown location.

After the publication of the first edition of *Alba ad Astra* in 2009, these pictures were sent anonymously to Madeleine Shepherd by a self-described "well-wisher". Thought at first to show the construction of the *Golden Eagle*, the visible evidence, such as it is, does not support this. The four images appear to record the construction of a cyclotron, a type of particle accelerator. However, this device would seem to have been intended to hold up to three operators or occupants. The disturbing implication is that these pictures document the assembly of a bootstrap time machine. Whether this has already happened or is yet to occur has not been determined.

✸✸ THE SCOTTISH OFFICE

Guy Mandersley, Esq.,
Tweedbrooke Design,
14 Chessels Mews
Edinburgh

4th September 1966

Dear Mr Mandersley,

With reference to our recent telephone
conversation, I confirm that you are authorised to
proceed with the promotional materials we discussed.
Payment will be in instalments against agreed stage
completions, again as discussed.

You asked for a detailed breakdown of the materials,
costs and designs that we outlined to you over lunch
yesterday. I regret that that is not possible under
any circumstances. As indicated to you this project
is proceeding in utmost secrecy and you for your
part must understand the sensitivity given the
identity of Expo 67's hosts.

Similarly, you must prepare yourself for the
possibility that this commission will never see the
light of day. It will only do so in the event of the
success of the main project it supports. With regard
to that, I regret I cannot be more specific than I
have been already.

You will however be given limited access to the
launch site and an opportunity to discuss matters in
general terms with Mr MacKracken, Mr Dent and
others. I will be in contact once the visit has been
arranged.

Yours sincerely,

G Purvis

[handwritten note:] Have call from Scot. Off wallah
— change of venue from
Moscow to Montreal
does <u>not</u> alter need for
extreme secrecy
These people are paranoid!!!

Expo 67 Materials

compiled and edited by
Kirsti Wishart

DRAFT SUBMISSION BY TWEEDBROOKE ASSOCIATES
ON THE PROPOSED SCOTTISH SPACE PROGRAMME
PAVILLION,
MOSCOW 1967
PROVISIONAL TITLE: ALBA AD ASTRA

Statement of Intent

After years of secrecy and experimentation, Scotland will finally
unveil its successful space programme at the 1967 Moscow Expo.
We at Tweedbrooke Associates regard the opportunity to design
a pavilion marking the inaugural flight of Europe's first manned
spacecraft, Golden Eagle, as a unique honour. As a result, we
have sought to devise a spectacle that fully celebrates the years
of work by Scottish scientists, engineers and military personnel
which are set to culminate in this magnificent achievement.

Since the world's attention has focused on the technological advances of the United States and the U.S.S.R., where better than this global event for the country famed as the birthplace of inventors such as John Logie Baird and Alexander Graham Bell to signal its entry into the space race. An occasion like this requires a bold and imaginative approach, one that seeks not only to commemorate the bravery of astronauts such as Bill MacKraken and his support team, but also to outline future branding opportunities for Scottish tourism, industry and culture. Some might think the attractions that follow "outlandish", but we would argue that this is an entirely fitting approach for a project that aims to take Scotland to the stars, that pushes the country's talent for innovation and exploration to its logical extreme.

Pavilion Design

Following brief access to sketches drawn by Basil Spence outlining the design for the proposed British Pavilion that feature a half-finished, spire-like column displaying the Union Flag, we would request an abstract representation of the Golden Eagle rocket displaying a Saltire to act as a suitable counterpoint. This would ensure an increase in numbers through the Scottish entrance, although we are aware that it may require careful negotiation with representatives of the other home nations.

Pavilion Forecourt

Passing through the entranceway and entering the exhibition forecourt, visitors will be greeted by a kinetic sculpture symbolising the combination of skilled engineering and refined aesthetics that led to the creation of Golden Eagle. As the wind catches its silver arms, causing them to move in graceful arcs echoing the parabolic flight of a spacecraft, sound is generated. The roar of a rocket launch, the static of radio contact, brief instructions from ground control, and the bleeps and hums of electronic controls are underscored by an unmistakably Scottish drone in a tone poem written by Scottish avant-garde composer Alexander Turnbull. He describes his composition as his "symphony of the stars, after Finnessey. With bagpipe choir."

Next to the sculpture, sightseers will have their first opportunity to sample the training undertaken by Scottish astronauts. In a light-hearted exhibit, they can enjoying freedom from gravity by bouncing around in the Weightless Space Bouncy Bubble Capsule (see illustrative model #1).

Display Room 1: Blast-off!

Visitors proceed to a darkened space illuminated by starlight and a cometary streak describing the trajectory of Golden Eagle across the firmament. If brave enough, they can then take a ride in the Scottish Space Flight Launch Simulator. Large enough to hold four passengers, the Simulator utilises the latest in fairground, film and cinema technology to recreate a rocket launch from the thrilling perspective of the astronaut.

Although the view available to actual astronauts is limited, combined footage from multiple cameras gives Simulator passengers the experience of sitting in a nose-cone made entirely of glass. Once strapped in, the radio crackles to life as the countdown starts and a gentle vibration begins. Then the trembling becomes a bone-shaking shudder as "We have blast-off!" is announced over the speaker in soft Highland tones.

The ground slowly spirals away as the passengers are rocked back in their seats. Their view expands as the horizon broadens out, curving across their field of vision and becoming the brilliant navy-blue boundary marking the limits of Earth's atmosphere. Then the upward trajectory stops and there is a brief pause – just time enough for the adventurers to catch their breath – before the capsule tips gently forward and falls back to earth as the screen fades to black.

(Please note, the simulator will not be suitable for those over the age of retirement, anyone with a heart or breathing condition, or those who are prone to hysteria. A medical professional should be on hand at all times.)

Display Room 2: The Northern Lights

For those of a nervous disposition, it will be a relief to enter the next section of the Pavilion, an area that replicates both the compact environs of the Golden Eagle flight capsule and the club room on the Alba ad Astra base, The Northern Lights, where crew members relax after a hard day's training. Tweedbrooke would like to sincerely thank the officials responsible for the relaxation of security protocol that enabled our designers to visit the extraordinary individuals who live and work there.

The seats displayed are exact replicas of those in the rocket and are upholstered in Harris tweed. This blend was created by the famed textile designer Bernat Klein, and combines a mix of blues and purples in tones suggestive of moorland heather, bluebells and thistles. Piping and other accents are worked in "space-age" tweed from Mrs Perrin of Stornoway. With its many flecks of silver, it conveys both a star-spangled night sky and the metallic fabrics of the astronauts' suits. (see illustrative samples #2 and #3). Explanatory notes inform visitors that tweed was employed not solely for patriotic reasons, but also for the purposes of health and safety owing to its slow-burning properties. To illustrate this, the back of one of the seats is slightly charred – this is a swatch rescued from the wreckage of an early prototype. As Bill MacKraken laconically explained to our researcher, "Imagine what a conflagration there would have been had there not been tweed in the cockpit and an unexpected shower that day." We believe this detail does much to convey the very real risks these men face every day while working on the project.

Although the homespun cosiness on display may come as a surprise, it serves a serious purpose by quietly emphasising the domestic features of the Scottish space programme. For example, the West Highland terrier who sits up alert in the basket beneath the flight control panel, head cocked, is indeed Keltie, kindly donated by trainee astronaut Lachlan Smart. The first Scottish dog to complete a full orbit of the Earth, she lived happily with Lachlan for several years until an unfortunate accident with a speeding push-bike. As Bill MacKraken has remarked, "Outer space was no bother for Keltie, but Dunfermline High Street wasn't such a walk in the park." The dog-collars, chains and photographs decorating the outside of the basket memorialise the achievements of all the other canine explorers who blazed a flight path for their owners.

An open roll-top desk holds some slightly scorched papers donated to by the Scottish Rocketry Society to remind us that that the work carried out by hobbyists indulging their pastime during weekends and holidays provided valuable insights, leading directly to the construction of Golden Eagle.

Scattered over occasional tables are items that indicate both the team spirit pervading the Alba ad Astra base and strong marketing opportunities. Mugs and ashtrays, cuff-links and tie-pins all display the triple-A emblem (see prototype sketch #4). The aim is to bring the astronauts "down to earth", as it were, allowing visitors to imagine them chatting in the club-room atmosphere, sipping from the bottle of The Angel's Share on the sideboard, a single-malt whisky created for the crew by a local distillery, its name displaying the typically dry Scottish sense humour. (An explanatory note will be provided for those of a non-Scottish or non-whisky-drinking persuasion: the "angel's share" refers to the 2% of whisky that evaporates as it matures in its cask.)

A dram provides a suitable accompaniment to the varieties of space food laid out on the small bar in their tinfoil wrappings. These have been manufactured to guarantee the astronauts a taste of home in gravity-free surroundings, and include freeze-dried haggis, stovies, mince and tatties, clootie dumplings, blocks of tablet, and Luca's ice-cream.

Display Room 3: The Future Unveiled

The final room appears at first glance to be an ordinary Scottish living room and kitchenette. Closer inspection reveals nothing down-to-earth about this household. Each item on display – from the coffee table and chairs to the wallpaper and lamps – has been produced by Scottish designers inspired by the example of the Scottish space pioneers. The grey and silver patterned wallpaper is, in fact, a map of the Moon, but each landmark has been renamed. Where once lay the Sea of Tranquillity or the Sea of Despair, we now find Loch Katrine and Loch Ness. The craters once called "Babbage" and "Schiller" have become "Barrie" and "Hogg". "Heidegger" has been ousted by "Hume".

Bulbous purple lampshades made of plastic combine both the forms of fanciful spaceships and thistle-heads. The polished top of a coffee table is constructed from same tempered Ravenscraig steel that lines the control room of Golden Eagle; its legs are modelled on the proposed moon landing capsule or "Wee Stoater", as it's referred to by the team. On the table a board game, From Saltcoats to Saturn!, is ready to be played. Contestants chose their rocket counter and begin their journey towards the launch pad, receiving booster points by hitting such squares as "Sponsorship from Tennent's secured, crates of 80/-

arrive at base!" or "Landing off Largs Bay successful, ice-cream in Nardini's!" Players have to avoid landing on "Scotland's team fails to reach World Cup Finals, national confidence slumps, funding slashed" or "Seagull strike results in aborted test flight, one collie lost".

A magazine rack holds copies of The People's Friend with articles including "How to Bake a Scone in Zero Gravity", "Kids Games to Play on Mars" and "How to Knit Your Own Spacesuit". The Sunday Post features interviews with the Alba ad Astra team and an exclusive "Broons" story in which Horace convinces his family he's won a place on Golden Eagle, while a new "Oor Wullie" adventure sees our cheeky hero sneak onto the base, have his bucket melted by a rocket blast-off and lose Wee Jeemy before realising, on seeing footage beamed down on television, that his pet has joined Bill MacKraken on Golden Eagle. (All of the above subject to approval from D. C. Thomson & Co.)

The dining table in the kitchenette shows an exclusive range of space-inspired treats: a Tunnock's "Space Station Set" featuring a rocket (Caramel Wafer), landing capsule (Teacake) and asteroid (Snowball); bottles of Barr's "Rocket Fuel"; a packet of Scott's Porage Oats with the mascot in full astronaut regalia; and free samples of MacCowan's latest experimental sweet, Atomic Space Dust (the popping of which can be heard from over half a mile away).

Display Room 4: Touchdown
The shop offers a number of collectable items as mementoes of this incredible endeavour, including a set of five Scottish Bluebell matchboxes illustrating the development of the national space programme from rockets used as part of an experimental Hebridean postal service to the launching of Keltie and

concluding with a group portrait of Bill MacKraken with the Golden Eagle support team.

(Posters of Eduardo Paolozzi's planned mural for Glasgow's Charing Cross underground station will also be available. With its laser-eyed robots, tentacled creatures and screaming blonde damsels in distress fleeing danger astride bright-red rocket-ships, the mural draws on the artist's fascination with sci-fi pop art while providing a clear time line illustrating the important moments in the development of the Alba ad Astra project.)

Conclusion

Tweedbrooke believes the exhibition outlined above will capture the exhilaration, drama and anticipation that the whole nation must experience when this latest frontier in Scottish exploration is revealed. Following in the intrepid spirit of thousands of Scots who left this country to populate to the New World, Australia and New Zealand, Alba ad Astra proves that even gravity can't hold back the Scots when they set their minds to achieving great things. We aim to leave visitors with little doubt that the first man to set foot on the moon will have a Scottish surname. We hope you share our vision.

A selection of Alba ad Astra artefacts and designs discovered in the Tweedbrooke archive including fabric samples, a knitting pattern, souvenir model rocket and sketches for the a visitor experience.

E-mail and Memos Leaked to Hector MacKraken

via Andrew C. Ferguson

From: [undisclosed source]

To: hector.mackraken@googlemail.com

Dear Mr MacKraken,

Firstly, please don't try to respond to this email as to do so may compromise national security.

You don't know me, and that will probably always be the case. However, it appears my father knew your father very well, and held secret information on his disappearance. On his deathbed three years ago, my father directed me to a box in the attic which held xeroxed copies of certain memos – photocopies of some of which I put through your door last night. He instructed me to find you and pass these on to you, saying to me that he felt he owed it to you "after such a long time".

There are two reasons why I need to be so secretive on this matter. The first is that I, like my father before me, am a civil servant. So was your father – at least, that's what it said in his letter of appointment. It could hardly say "astronaut" explicitly. He, like my father and myself, had to sign the Official Secrets Act, and

I am in all likelihood breaching at least three sections of it by communicating this to you.

The second reason for my secrecy should be self-evident from the content of the memoranda.

It will of course be a matter for you what you choose to do with this material. I would caution you, however, that if you go to the press you will be ridiculed and portrayed as a pathetic figure in thrall to fool's gold of conspiracy theories. The most favourable reaction you can expect will be pity for the loss of your father at an early age. I state this simply as a fact, as I know only too well how such things can be manipulated and reputations destroyed.

One last thing: my father entrusted me with an additional secret – the key to a listening station on the East Lothian coast. He would only say that, whatever it was listening for, it was still "operative", and that I should check on it from time to time. In between my intermittent search for you, and the sundry other things I have to occupy my time, I have driven out along the coast. I can't tell you where it is, of course, but it's sufficiently inaccessible and well hidden amongst the dunes to have survived. In it, a small machine of a very outdated design sits. On my first visit, it was suspiciously free of dust and cobwebs. Perhaps my father had maintained it until his last illness.

The ticker-tape output on the device has never moved – until, that is, last month, when it spat out a couple of notches of paper, clearly distinguishable from the yellowed links already hanging from it. That fact may of course be utterly meaningless, but it did, at least, prompt me to finally track down both your postal and email addresses.

Whatever you do next, be very careful. You do not have to be a conspiracy theorist to believe that not all agencies of the state are subjected to public scrutiny all the time.

-A Well-Wisher

20th July, 1966

CONFIDENTIAL — RECIPIENT ONLY

from: George Purvis,

     Senior Assistant Under Secretary to the
Secretary of State

     to: Philip Dent, Pumping Station
Project Director

I write to inform you that I have just
returned from an extremely uncomfortable
meeting with the Minister. Although the current
Government is prepared to continue funding the
project at existing levels, there is a degree of
nervousness about the implications politically
if it all goes wrong — and, frankly, given the
current Nationalist surge, even if it all goes
right. The Plaid Cymru result in Carmarthen has
rendered other regions such as Scotland into an
extremely febrile state at present.

     I urge you therefore to proceed with caution
and in utmost secrecy.

3rd November, 1966

CONFIDENTIAL — RECIPIENT ONLY

from: George Purvis,

     Senior Assistant Under Secretary to the
Secretary of State

     to: Philip Dent, Pumping Station
Project Director

With reference to yours of 14th inst., I can confirm that there is clearance for MacKraken to be occupant of the "vehicle". He appears to be utterly sound, and may be trusted not to reveal details of the project to anyone. No known affiliations with any political organisations.

I note what you say about launch being imminent, and at Ministerial level the will is there to go ahead. However, I cannot stress enough that this project must remain classified until we are assured of its success. Any form of failure will render us, and by extension, the British nation, an object of ridicule internationally.

4th November, 1966

from: George Purvis,

Senior Assistant Under Secretary to the Secretary of State

to: Philip Dent, Pumping Station Project Director

I understand the launch has been brought forward to tomorrow night, to accommodate a weather window. Whilst this may have attendant benefits — any witnesses tomorrow night will presumably imagine they are seeing some form of giant firework — I would, as ever, urge caution.

I would also take this opportunity to express my hope for a successful outcome, and the safe return of MacKraken from the project.

3rd December, 1966

CONFIDENTIAL — RECIPIENT ONLY

from: George Purvis,

     Senior Assistant Under Secretary to the Secretary of State

     to: Philip Dent, Pumping Station Project Director

Dear Mr Dent,

I write simply to inform you that, following my downgrading from Senior Assistant Under Secretary to Assistant to the Senior Assistant Under Secretary, future correspondence on this matter should be directed to Mr Bradley, the Senior Assistant Under Secretary.

My last involvement in this project is to authorise a transfer of the final tranche of project funding to your budget heading. This is on the strict understanding that it will be as you say used for compensatory measures in relation to Mrs MacKraken and her son.

Please note that the Works Division will be with you shortly, if they are not so already, to carry out the necessary dismantling. The various items of equipment per the inventory you so helpfully supplied shall be distributed to different locations to aid their assimilation into the landscape.

You are to report to St Andrews House on Monday for reassignment. I understand that your new duties will be somewhat different.

The Last Man in Space?

Andrew J. Wilson

You can always triangulate the coordinates of the best pub in town if your known points of reference are an author with an understanding of science, and a researcher who appreciates the craft of writing. On a good night, you'll then find the shortest distance to your chosen watering hole by following the trail of the science fiction fans. As Alfred Bester very nearly wrote, The Bars My Destination.

Pliny the Elder gave us in vino veritas – cheerfully paraphrasing or perhaps even plagiarising the Greek poet Alcaeus – and there have been many memorable quotes about drinking ever since. Winston Churchill, no less, said rather pointedly, "Always remember that I have taken more out of alcohol than alcohol has taken out of me." And I'm always moved when I think about Frida Kahlo's observation: "I tried to drown my sorrows, but the bastards learned how to swim, and now I am overwhelmed by this decent and good feeling."

For the truth of the matter, I refer you to the 2000-year-old wisdom of Seneca the Younger: "Drunkenness is simply voluntary insanity," the old Stoic said, and I'm inclined to agree. We all need to let off a little steam from time to time, especially after contemplating the mysteries of the universe, whether by means of a radio telescope or through the blank screen of a word processor.

In my home city of Edinburgh, the preferred haunt of the three "Rs" – readers, writers and researchers – varies as pubs change hands, and the quality of the ales on tap and the single malts behind the bar goes up or down. Over the years, we've met all across the centre of town, but my favourite haunt will always be the Major Weir.

Tucked away in the depths of the Old Town, near the bottom of a cobbled side-street, the place isn't much to look at from the outside. Its coat of paint is peeling, and the view of the interior is obscured by deeply unfashionable bottle-bottom windowpanes. In fact, you'd walk right past the place if you didn't know better. But behind the creaking double doors, the Major Weir is a warren that burrows deep under the Royal Mile. It's a free house, of course, which means that the landlord stocks what he likes – and what he likes is to sell drinks, so if he doesn't have your particular poison, you'll find it the next time you visit, if you ask nicely.

Many curious characters mingle in that unreconstructed maze of snugs and spiralling steps. This isn't a workmen's bar, although some drink there. It's not an academics' watering hole, although their voices can be heard. And it's not a youngsters' rendezvous, although a few of the customers can only just be over the legal drinking age. The speciality of the Major Weir is storytelling. We gather there on a Thursday when we can, and we fit right in.

I'll give you an example: One evening, we were talking about pen names for some reason. Banksie, of course, boasts about using "the world's most transparent pseudonym" for his science fiction, simply inserting his middle initial between his first and last names. My old friend Dr S_____ L_____ (there's no need for the anonymization, I just love that kind of old-fashioned coyness) adopted Bingo T. MacArthur back in our fanzine days, long before he became a full-time astronomer. I even flip-flopped my own name to create William Anderson when I had to review the same book twice.

Well, I have to admit that things got rather sillier as the drinks were drunk and the rounds kept coming round. We began to invent noms de plume after Steve Glover pointed out that Charlie Stross's name is an anagram of Crass Holsters. I came up with Luther Kant and Primo Leviathan, and the next thing we knew, we had Benedict Quisling, Pollyanna Discharge and Milton Embolism... Even e. e. "doc" cummings (all in lower case, naturally) was floated and then sunk without a trace.

This was Seneca's "voluntary insanity", of course – we'd need a good pseudonym for some of the ideas we toyed with that night. Someone mentioned an unfilmable and quite probably unprintable idea for Doctor Who entitled "Planet of the Bastards", and that steered us into the contentious area of remakes or so-called re-imaginings. Mike Holmes, who troubles the websites of the local papers as a Friend of Fernando Poo, suggested that it was high time someone took a crack at Space: 1999. Banksie exploded: The bad science was unforgivable! It must never be remade!

Well, that was like a red rag to a bullshitter, so I came up with an outline for Space: 2099 on the spot.

"The crew of the moonbase aren't burying radioactive waste," I said. "Oh no, while extracting ice from one of the poles, they find ancient ruins and begin to excavate the site..."

"Okay..." said Steve.

"The problem is," I went on, improvising wildly, "the Moon isn't a moon. It's a disabled alien war machine that's been lying dormant in Earth's orbit for millions of years – and they've reactivated it! The warp drive fires up and the Moon jumps to the next target programmed into its memory banks... Here's the logline: The last battle in a billion-year-old intergalactic war is about to be fought – and humanity has to decide which side it's on!"

"KO," said Mike.

Ken laughed out loud and even Banksie liked it. Someone suggested – not me, I assure you – that since we'd come up with this re-imagining in Scotland and most of us had been born north of the border, the characters should be Scottish too... Then things took a strange turn.

"The problem with Scots," said an old but elegant man, "is that we tend to snatch defeat from the jaws of victory."

"Excuse me?" I replied. The stranger had appeared out of nowhere, much like his non sequitur, and now he was sitting down at our table uninvited, commandeering the last free stool.

"Admit it, gentlemen," he insisted. "It's true."

The new member of our circle had the look of a retired civil servant. He wore a neat, if unfashionable, three-piece suit, and sported a superfluous goatee that might have been grown for a bet.

"I'm sorry," I said, "I didn't catch your name."

"Call me Hugh," he replied. "In the spirit of your earlier badinage, I'll adopt an alias. Call me Hugh Mann." Our groans didn't put him off. "I apologise for the pun, but it's probably politic for me to conceal my identity. You see, as I said, the Scots have a terrible habit of dropping the ball – and not just during rugby internationals. Watt, Baird and Fleming gave us the steam engine, television and penicillin, respectively, but our benighted nation has never become the technological powerhouse it should have been. What's worse is that some of our most astounding achievements have been – what's the word nowadays – redacted from history ... because they ended in disaster."

We smelled a rat, but let Mr Mann continue. After all, you have to set your trap and then wait patiently before you can catch an offending rodent.

"I must say that your comical idea of Scots in space is not original," he said, "but there's no way any of you could have known that."

"Please, Hugh," I said, priming the rat trap, "do go on."

The old man smiled and launched into his tale.

"In the district of Angus, you can still see the shell of Lord Strathbungo's Improved Skyrocket Manufactory. Nothing more than ruins now, but in its time, the place promised Scotland the stars, if not the world. His Lordship was a polymath and entrepreneur who became an enthusiastic student of those pioneering rocket scientists of the 1920s, men whose names I can never remember how to pronounce."

"Konstantin Tsiolkovsky and Hermann Oberth?" Ken suggested.

"Quite so. Strathbungo envisaged a multitude of both commercial and experimental applications for rocketry, but he died – along with a number of his staff – in an accident involving concentrated nitric acid that occurred around the time of the Wall Street Crash. His papers were left to the Scottish Rocketry Society, but were confiscated by the Crown, which is how I found out about this neglected fragment of history.

"Now, the Scottish Rocketry Society was a ragtag group of amateur enthusiasts who, despite spending most of their time in one pub or another, performed some experimental trials in the Campsie Fells in the 1930s. They were inspired by Robert Goddard, of course, but I believe that they were equally enthused by Wells and Verne, not to mention the garish American pulp magazines that arrived as ballast on transatlantic cargo vessels. Mind you, the drink might have had something to do with it too. These dedicated devotees put their limited resources to remarkable use. Several small projectiles were successfully fired from the concrete launch pad that they built high up in the hills. I even saw a few copies of their newsletter, Rocketry Scotland, which was published into the 1960s. The National Library of Scotland has an almost-complete run."

I made a mental note to check on this later, if I had the time.

"The outbreak of the Second World War saw the end of such attempts to emulate Goddard, of course, but many of those who gave up so much of their spare time and disposable income would find themselves called up to serve their country by working on the military applications of their hobby."

The trap needed bait, so I bought my round and stood Hugh a drink.

"During the war," he went on, "the government devised a fall-back strategy that was to be implemented if Operation Sea Lion, the Nazis' planned invasion of England, succeeded. A new front was to be established along the border with Scotland. The military's ultra-top-secret missile programme, spearheaded by many conscripted Scottish rocketry enthusiasts, was intended to form the last line of defence – or attack – in such an extremity.

"Our men worked all over the country, particularly on the

test range on Barra, and came up with the Z-1 flying bomb one long, whisky-fuelled night. The 'Buzzard', as they called it, was intended to be a primitive atomic missile. There was to be no warhead since the explosion caused by the hydrogen-fuelled rocket's impact with the intended target would be more than sufficient..."

We stared at him in disbelief.

"Come now, gentlemen, as you should know, Fermi achieved nuclear fission as early as 1934, and he created a criticality with Szilard only eight years later. I never suggested that the Scots invented any of this...

"Anyway, we can all be thankful that their work never reached completion – never mind saw use in anger – but this clandestine endeavour continued into the Cold War. While the Blue Streak was developed south of the border, the cream of the Caledonian rocketeers concentrated on their own project, led by a young man named Fraser Ferguson. The English ballistic missile used liquid oxygen and kerosene as propellants, but it had at least twice the overall gross lift-off mass of the Scottish alternative. The project was a dead end, which explains its termination. On the other hand, as Ferguson said, 'We Scots knew that the way onwards and upwards must be nuclear'..." Hugh paused dramatically. "Oh dear, my mouth is rather dry. Could someone get me a glass of water, please?"

"I suppose you'd like a little whisky in that?" I asked. He smiled and nodded, while pointing out that Old Pulteney was the Major Weir's Malt of the Moment. Banksie did the honours.

"Well, to cut a long story short – and one that I've had to piece together over the years at that – our canny Scots developed a manned nuclear rocket at last. They obtained the fuel rods they needed from the Chapelcross Magnox nuclear power plant in Annan. Officially, the primary purpose of Chapelcross was to produce weapons-grade plutonium for the British nuclear weapons programme while also generating power for the National Grid, but it always had a third and wholly secret purpose. Ferguson obtained his test pilot, one Flight Lieutenant William MacKraken, on an extended loan from the Royal Air Force."

"And how did this potential death-trap work?" Ken asked.

"Oh, it looked very much like the torpedo-shaped rocket ships from the films of the period, fins and all, with the exception of the turbine vents that drew the air in to give the engine some reaction mass once the initial payload of liquid hydrogen had done its job. The faster the craft went, the more air was taken in until it began to leave the atmosphere. At that point, ball bearings made of Cornish tin were released explosively to hurl the contraption into orbit... Well, that was the plan."

"So the rocket never flew?" Steve asked.

"Oh no, quite the contrary, it did, and only too well," Hugh replied. "It wasn't supposed to, of course –it was launched more or less accidentally during a test firing at Woomera in 1966. Flight Lieutenant MacKraken was on board."

This time, I was the one who needed another drink. Thankfully, Charlie obliged.

"It was a tragedy – still is. The ship was a masterpiece of contemporary engineering, but it was still limited by the technology of the time. The controls were almost all mechanical, and there were no computers back then, of course. MacKraken was in the cockpit, if that's what you'd call the cramped compartment, and the intention was simply to test-fire the motor on the ground. The controls regulating the core jammed. The reactor began to go critical. The military observers from the

Australian Defence Force made it quite clear that they would not tolerate a nuclear accident on Antipodean soil. The technicians were panicking, but MacKraken insisted on taking off. He knew that a launch was the only way to avert disaster. He was a very, very brave man.

"The ship blasted off all right, but then it went off course, of course. The Scots had desperately tried to plot an orbital trajectory that would bring their man back safely, but they were using nothing more than slide rules and graph paper, probably at gunpoint. Someone or other misplaced a decimal point and the rocket never came down. The telemetrists calculated that years would pass before it began to make its return journey..."

"What a way to go," I said. "Do you know what happened in the end?"

"In the end?" Hugh asked. "I don't know if the story is over yet. The whole terrible business was covered up, obviously, and then almost all the records were either shredded, burned or buried in landfill. But what goes around comes around, as they say.

"When I worked for – well, let's call it the British Non-Ferrous Metals Research Association – I ran into a man called Harry Purvis, who told me a thing or two about what had happened, details that never appeared in the records. It was rumoured that one member of mission control, allegedly Fraser Ferguson, identified the mistake just after it was too late to correct, and calculated how long MacKraken's round trip would be. He told the flight lieutenant to cut the oxygen and life support, open his pressure suit, blow the seals on the pipes carrying the liquid hydrogen and ... flash-freeze himself. The doomed man would die, but Ferguson argued, it might be possible to bring him back to life one day...

"And so the long wait for his homecoming began, and slowly but surely, the small number of folk who knew the truth dwindled as time took its inevitable toll. I was only able to piece together the sad history of Scotland's misadventures in rocketry with the help of Harry Purvis, and it was through him that I was inducted into the secret society of veterans led by Fraser Ferguson who watched the skies for the day when MacKraken might return. Are any of you familiar with the outpost at Tantallon?"

"You mean the experimental radar and listening station in East Lothian?" Banksie asked. "The one only visible from the River Forth? Built during World War II and operational until the mid-sixties, wasn't it? I remember reading about it when all that bumf was made available under the Freedom of Information Act."

Hugh nodded. "Although supposedly decommissioned in the 1960s," he said, "it was, in fact, repurposed over time by Ferguson with the help of others such as myself ... and funds siphoned off from Cold War black budgets. Until recently, the equipment was maintained and monitored on a semi-regular basis. In the end, after Fraser's death, that task fell to me alone."

"What do you mean?" I prompted. It was last orders both at the bar and for Hugh's tale.

"After I officially retired, I persuaded some contacts at Edinburgh University to perform a few calculations on a pro bono basis. They determined that, if a hypothetical nuclear rocket suffered a runaway chain reaction, then it would not only have left Earth's orbit, but continued on a parabolic course that would have taken it beyond the orbit of Neptune and through the Kuiper Belt at the edge of the solar system. 'At sufficient velocities,' their report stated, 'interplanetary dust and ice crystals scooped up by the propulsion system's air vents would act as a perfectly adequate reaction mass.'

"Working hypothetically on a number of assumptions that that I suggested based on Fraser Ferguson's notes, my contacts predicted that the spacecraft would return to Earth almost half a century after its departure. In the circumstances, I assumed that Flight Lieutenant MacKraken's remains would finally be cremated when his ship inevitably burned up in the Earth's atmosphere..."

The bar staff were collecting glasses and encouraging us to leave, but Hugh hadn't quite finished.

"I persuaded my friends at the university to allow me some telescope time at the observatory so that I could watch the bitter end of the whole sorry affair. Ferguson's notes were accurate and I pinpointed the craft ... only to witness the thing rotating, clearly firing its retro-rockets to initiate course corrections and deceleration procedures. Of course, there could be no possibility that the pilot was still alive, could there? But if MacKraken wasn't at the controls, then who or what was?"

Hugh gave us a look so pointed he could have nailed us to the wall.

"And those, I'm afraid, are all the facts at my disposal," he said. "Anything else can only be speculation, which you gentlemen are far better equipped to supply than I am..."

"Extraterrestrial intelligence?" Banksie suggested.

"Extremophile nanobacteria?" Ken countered.

"One hundred per cent pure, undiluted unobtanium?" Charlie concluded.

"Perhaps one of you is right, perhaps all of you are to one degree or another," the old man said thoughtfully. "One thing's for certain, MacKraken must have encountered something or other out there in deep space. Fraser Ferguson had hoped that time would supply the means to bring our friend back to life. Little did he know – how could he? – that space itself would provide the solution in the end."

We had to go, but I decided to walk Hugh back up the road.

"You don't really expect us to believe any of that, do you?" I asked.

He stopped and smiled at me oddly. "Frankly, I don't care whether you do or you don't. 'Truth will out,' according to the Bard, and as he also wrote in Hamlet, 'There are more things in heaven and earth ... than are dreamt of in your philosophy...' I've filled the ample free time that my retirement allows me by looking for the spot where the last man in space returned to Earth."

"Good luck with that," I told him, turning to head home, but he caught me by the arm. His grip was surprisingly firm.

"Not so fast, laddie," Hugh said. "I found the place. The capsule washed up on Barra. It was empty by the time I got there, but scrawled on the inside of the hull were two words, words repeated over and over again – 'PAY' and 'BACK'..."

I could imagine the graffiti covering the cockpit walls:

PAY	BACK	PAY	BACK	PAY	BACK	PAY
BACK	PAY	BACK	PAY	BACK	PAY	BACK
PAY	BACK	PAY	BACK	PAY	BACK	PAY
BACK	PAY	BACK	PAY	BACK	PAY	BACK
PAY	BACK	PAY	BACK	PAY	BACK	PAY
BACK	PAY	BACK	PAY	BACK	PAY	BACK
PAY	BACK	PAY	BACK	PAY	BACK	PAY
BACK	PAY	BACK	PAY	BACK	PAY	BACK
PAY	BACK	PAY	BACK	PAY	BACK	PAY
BACK	PAY	BACK	PAY	BACK	PAY	BACK

"Here's tae us," I said, invoking an old Scottish toast as we watched the stars turn overhead. "Wha's like us?"

"Damn few," Hugh replied, "an' they're a' deid!"

Then he went on his way, leaving me to decide whether MacKraken's mysterious scrawl was a statement of vengeful intent, or the flight lieutenant's reminder to himself that Her Majesty's Government owed him a colossal amount of money. Perhaps, I decided, that would be revenge enough in itself.

– For Madeleine Shepherd.

THE JURA RECOVERY

Ken MacLeod

"Do you believe in all that, then?"

Any science fiction writer will tell you that's the question they most expect when they admit their trade. Taxi drivers are particularly apt to chuck this one over their shoulder. (The first to ask me it went on: "I had that Erich Von Daniken in the back once.") But it can come from anyone who isn't a science fiction reader - which, of course, means most people.

This time, it came from the weathered-looking bloke beside me at the bar of the Jura Hotel. I'd just finished my fish and chips and was settling into my second pint when he'd struck up the conversation. Apart from two campers eating their dinner and sitting right against the far window - no doubt because it was the only place they could get so much as a glimmer of mobile phone reception - we were alone in the bar. We'd introduced ourselves, and got talking about our respective jobs. His name was Hamish - I didn't catch the surname - and like many islanders he did several jobs: a bit of building work in the summer; driving a quad-bike and doing this and that up on one of the shooting estates; and a lot of evenings out on his boat, catching lobsters and langoustines. I told him about my considerably less arduous calling, and how I had been given a week's stay at the Jura Lodge in exchange for one short story, in my own genre.

And, of course, he'd winkled the genre out of my shell.

"All what?" I asked, though I knew.

"Little green men," Hamish said. He twiddled a forefinger above his head. "Flying saucers. Life on other worlds."

"No, I don't," I said. "I mean, I wouldn't rule out life - even intelligent life - elsewhere in the galaxy, but I don't think it's visiting us, and if it is, UFOs are very unlikely to be evidence of anything like it."

"So you do believe in aliens," he said.

"It's not a question of *believing*," I said, slightly irritated. (This is another patch of well-trodden ground.) "It's a question of evidence. All the evidence we have - about life on Earth, and about other planets - suggests that the conditions for life may exist on some planets around other stars. So I'll allow the possibility - the probability, even - of life somewhere else. But all the evidence about UFOs that I've seen, and I've looked at a lot, tells me they're almost all mistakes or hoaxes or - OK, just maybe - some unknown phenomenon in the atmosphere. Not alien spacecraft."

"Why not?" He sounded interested. "Supposing they're something unknown, I mean."

"Well," I said, trying to avoid a sigh, "you'd think aliens who could cross light-years would find it easy enough to either contact us - land on the White House lawn, as the saying goes

- or to make sure we didn't know they were there at all. They wouldn't be doing the sort of things UFOs are supposed to - close encounters with farmers on back country roads, sort of thing."

Hamish cocked his head and thought about that. He took a sip of his pint, and gazed off into the mirror behind the bar.

"Aye, well," he said. "You might have a point about that. Doesn't matter, anyway." He looked over his shoulder, saw we were still alone at the bar - the barmaid was around the other side, waiting on the more formal diners in the lounge - and shrugged. "I don't *believe* in them, either. I've seen one."

"A UFO?"

He shook his head. "An alien."

Uh-uh, I thought. And he'd seemed such a normal, sensible guy. It reminded me of the bad luck I used to have when I moved to London. Every time I and any Scottish friend sat down in a bar, we'd unerringly find ourselves beside - or joined by - a drunk compatriot, eager to bend our ears about tarmac, penicilin, television, and other tokens of the great past and future of the country we (and he, many years earlier) had left for better opportunities.

"Ye-es," I said. "Uh, where was that?"

He jerked a thumb towards the dark window nearest us. "Out there, on the Sound, one night about a year ago."

"Right," I said. "So ... how come you saw an alien, out on the water, and not a UFO? Was it swimming or something?"

"Oh, no," he said. "It was in a spacecraft, all right. Not an alien spacecraft, though. One of ours."

I was trying hard not to laugh. "NASA? ESA?"

"No, no," he said. "One of *ours*. Scottish. Or maybe just

British, I don't know. One of the local ones, anyway."

I grinned at him, relieved. "Come on, you're winding me up. I know what this is about. You know about that wee spoof thing I did, about the secret Scottish space programme."

"Spoof thing?" He started rolling a cigarette.

"Aye," I said. "A booklet - a catalogue of an exhibition a few friends of mine in Edinburgh did a couple of years ago. Madeleine Shepherd, she's a photographer, and she took some photos of odd objects and places that looked like they were secret sites or parts of rockets and so on. A guy called Andrew Wilson and a few others wrote up a story around it, with fake documents and everything, and I wrote the introduction. All pretending to take it seriously, you know? Part of the Festival."

He shook his head. "Never heard of it," he said. "And I'm not winding you up. I'll tell you about it in a minute, after I've nipped outside."

That week, I was experimenting with an electronic cigarette, but this wasn't the time or place. I shook my almost-full pack of normal cigarettes, and reached for my lighter.

"I'll join you," I said.

We went out the back door and stood in its eave, facing the distillery across the island's main road. Drizzle sifted down past the street-lamp lights, which gleamed on the wet black road. Night had fallen in the hour since I'd last lit up, in the little car-park at the shore, on my way over from the Lodge to the Hotel. Something in the distillery sighed like a large and contented beast, exhaling vapour. Hamish and I did much the same.

"So," I said. "You were saying."

"Aye," he said. "Well. It was about a year ago, like I said. A clear night though, not a night like this. I was out on the boat with the lad, Andy, and we were working our way round the lobster creels. Andy was hauling them up, and I was at the wheel, keeping an eye on the radar and the GPS—"

"You have GPS?" I asked, impressed.

"Och, just on my iPhone, but it's good enough for getting from one marker buouy to another. Anyway, one eye on the instruments, another on the water. Clear, calm, not even much of a swell. And I was bringing her around when I catch a light in the sky, in the west, above the Paps of Jura. Thought it was an aeroplane at first, like you do. But it was moving too fast, and coming down. Couldn't have been more than thirty seconds before it was dropping down to the sea, and not that far in front of us by the look of it. I thought I was seeing a smallish plane coming down, maybe a forced landing or maybe a crash.

" 'Andy,' " I say, " 'take a look at that.' " By the time he's turned around, the light's coming down more slowly, and it's going from side to side at the same time, like it's swinging on a rope."

Hamish mimicked the action with the glowing tip of his roll-up.

"Andy figured out what we were seeing the same time as I did. 'It's on a parachute!' he said. I could see the blip on the radar by now, and it would have been about half a mile in front of us. 'Got the creels secure?' I asked him. 'Aye,' he says. 'Hold on to your hat, then,' I told him, and I gunned the engine. Then I got the binocs out and peered ahead. Dark night, no moon, nothing but the stars and the lights from Craighouse along the shore, and from the lighthouses. I think it was a lighthouse beam that caught it, and for a split second I could see it clear as day, a big white parachute with some wee thing swinging on the end of it. Then the next sweep of the beam didn't show it at all, and maybe I just imagined I saw the splash.

"Anyway, steady as she goes I thought, and I put the binocs down and steered for the thing. When we were about a fifty metres away from it I told Andy to turn the searchlight on it, and throttled back on the engine. I could see the parachute in the water like a huge jellyfish, and this thing like a big marker buoy - a yellow cone sticking out of the water, with a flat top. But it couldn't be just that.

"I flicked the radio to the emergency channel and started scanning. Sure enough, there was an automatic distress call going out, and it was giving the right location.

"So I moved closer in, close as I could get without bumping into the thing. Turned into the current, got the engine running just right to hold her in place. By now we're so close the searchlight's only picking out part of it, and I can see there's a hatch on the side.

" 'By Jove!' I say to Andy. 'It's a space capsule!' He shoots me a funny look and says: 'What's a space capsule?' And that from a lad with Highers! When I was in primary school I covered my jotters with doodles of capsules and rockets and spacemen."

"Me too," I said.

"So," Hamish went on, "I told the laddie about Gemini and Mercury and he just laughs. 'That thing's too effing primitive to be a space capsule,' he says.

" 'Look at it,' I said. 'See these black marks? They're scorch marks, from the heat of re-entry.'

" 'Aye, right,' he says. There wasn't much I could say to that, so we both shut up and looked at the thing, bobbing there in the water, and I was just thinking I should get on the blower to the Coast Guard or the lifeboat station at Craighouse when we heard banging from inside. There wasn't much noise, you see, just the thrum of the engine holding us steady in the drift, and the waves slapping the side of the thing, and we could hear the banging clear enough. I thought at the time it sounded like somebody knocking with a big spanner. And it sounded, you know, urgent.'

Hamish drew hard on his cigarette.

"So I said to Andy, 'There's someone inside wanting out.' 'Maybe there is,' he said, 'but I think we should wait for the rescue.' 'What rescue?' I say. 'If it's a space capsule, there'll be planes coming looking for it,' Andy said. 'I can't hear any planes,' I said. 'And whoever's in there might be suffocating for all we know. Tell you what, you take the wheel, hold her steady, get on the horn to the lifeboat boys, and I'll see if I can open yon hatch.'

"Now, you might be wondering why I didn't move the boat closer. I didn't want to, it was enough of a job holding her in place, and I had a trick up my sleeve. The boat's so small it doesn't need a dinghy, but we do have - well, we did have - a wee rubbish raft stowed by the stern. And I mean rubbish: a couple of floats made of long blocks of polystyrene with a couple of planks fixed across them, catamaran style. I had my waterproofs and my lifejacket on. I chucked the raft in the water, holding onto its rope, kicked off my wellies, grabbed the paddle and climbed on and sat on the planks, feet in the water. Water's bloody cold but I didn't expect to be in it for long. Couple of strokes of the paddle and I was alongside the capsule. It had a sort of shelf all around it under the water, and I thought about jumping on but that struck me as a bit foolhardy. So I worked my way round to beside the hatch, and I saw it had a handle. I could just about reach it by leaning over, half getting up off the seat, really awkward like, nearly tipping the raft over and just about pitching me into the sea, but I used one hand to steady myself on the side of the thing and the other to pull the handle. And then ..."

Hamish stubbed the end of his cigarette into the wall-mounted ashtray by the hotel door. Then, silently, as if thinking, he rolled another. I didn't particularly want to light up again, but I did anyway, sharing the flame.

"And then what?' I asked.

"And then it was like everything happened at once. The hatch flies open, and something comes flying out. It looked like a monkey, but green and kind of warty—"

"Oh, come on!" I said. "A little green man?"

Hamish looked me right in the eye. "I only saw it for a second or two, but that's what I saw. I felt it, and all. It hit me feet-first on the shoulder and knocked me off balance, and I sort of teetered for a moment and then down I went into the water. Came within an inch of knocking myself out on the side of the capsule - just missed it. Next thing I know, I'm treading water and flailing about, and I can just see the raft scooting away from me. The wee green devil was squatting on the planks and paddling away like nobody's business, off towards the Jura shore.

"Andy threw me a rope and I hauled myself back over the side of our boat. Dripping wet, not feeling the cold so much because I was still in the first shock. I looked back at the capsule, and saw the head and shoulders of a guy poking out of the hatch. He had a space helmet on, with the visor up, and he was sort of gasping, great big deep breaths we could hear across the maybe fifty feet between us.

"And then we heard something else. A chopper, closing fast. In a minute or so a big Sea King was hovering right above us, lighting up everything, and a winchman coming down to grab the spaceman, who'd by then clambered all the way out, shut the hatch, and was standing on that shelf I mentioned, sort of pressing himself spread-eagled back against the side. The winchman reached him, he leaned forward, the winchman slung a loop of rope around his back and up they went in a bear-hug, and into the chooper.

"The Sea King didn't hang around. It tilted forward a bit and just roared off, then climbed and headed away to the south-east. Left us staring with our mouths open, I can tell you, and the capsule just bobbing there in the water. I remember noticing the parachute semed to have drifted away and was sinking - I guess the lines blew off as the hatch opened, something automatic.

"I turned to Andy and I said, 'Let's get after that thing on the raft. We can find it with the searchlight if we get a move on.' He looked at me like I was daft. 'No effing way,' he says. 'You get your wet clothes off and get the space blanket around you before you effing catch effing pneumonia.' And he just turned away, took the wheel and steered for Craighouse. I did as I was told. Funny how we still call it the space blanket. Funny thing too, we had a good catch that night, and I made sure Andy got it all landed and into the truck before I let him drive me home. Told my wife I'd fallen in and she gave me an earful for nearly catching my death and being so careless at my age."

"You didn't say anything about—?"

"Not a word to anyone, apart from you."

He flicked his roll-up onto the black road, where it fizzed out. "Speaking of cold, I'm freezing. Reckon you owe me a dram."

"Reckon I do," I said.

We went back in and chased the residue of our pints with Jura malt.

"So you never, uh, investigated further?" I asked, after I'd bought Hamish a second dram, this time of 16-year-old.

"I didn't say that," he said. He swirled the whisky, took an appreciative sniff and sip, and made a judicious addition of water, setting the jug back carefully on the bar. "Oh, I didn't talk about what had happened. Neither did young Andy, as far as I know - and if he knows what's good for him, he won't. But I asked around, as you do. People see things they don't talk about much. Other fishermen, here and there up and down the coast. Gamekeepers on the estates." He tapped the side of his nose. "And I heard a few things."

"Yes?" I said, agog.

Hamish glanced over his shoulder. The campers were gone, and we were again alone.

"You know that secret Scottish space programme you talked about? It's real all right. The missile tests off Barra - rocket launches! All those mobile phone masts - a lot of them are part of the control system. That's why we never get any bars on our phones around here. Ninety percent of the capacity of yon mast on the hill back of the distillery there goes into tracking rockets. Same goes for the windmills going up all over the place. They *say* they're for electricity, but you look at the figures, they don't add up. Half of them are radars or the like. And the way they move rocket fuel around the Highlands without anyone noticing? They use whisky tankers as a cover. I'm telling you, man, it's all hidden in plain sight."

"Why should it be a secret?"

"Ah! Now there's a question. What I've heard, and I'm not saying it's true, mind, is that the British government has known for a long time that there are aliens. And they're in touch with them. Real, actual, little green men, like the one that jumped me. Nobody else knows, not the Yanks or the Russians for sure. It's the one thing we have that they don't, and it might come in handy some day."

"Handy?" I said. "How? Come on, what could be more handy than announcing you've made the greatest discovery of all time?"

Hamish shook his head. "It's a dangerous world we live in, as well you know, being a science fiction writer. Some day it might be very handy indeed to spring a surprise like that, if you happened to need some allies from the far side of the Moon."

"The Moon?" I said, stupidly. "You mean that's where the aliens are? Do they have a base there, or what?"

"I've said too much already," said Hamish. He knocked back his single malt and stood up, shrugging into his jacket. "Thanks for the dram, and I'll see you around."

I haven't seen him since.

On the way back to the Lodge - it's about a minute's stroll from the hotel - I walked to the end of the car park down by the shore, where there was an off-chance I could pick up messages on my mobile. The screen showed a couple of bars. I checked my email, phoned my wife - who was due to join me in three days for the weekend of my stay - and after we'd said goodnight I put the phone away and lit a last cigarette before turning in. The drizzle had stopped, and I could see a few stars. The Craighouse pier was off to the right, just past the hotel, and about a hundred yards from where I stood. The end of the pier was floodlit: a truck was parked there, and the quay's crane was lifting crates from a boat moored alongside. Silhouetted figures moved in the light.

As I gazed at the unloading and pondered Hamish's incredible tale, I noticed something odd. Out over the dark water, between the lights on the pier and flash of the harbour light on the headland of the small island across from it, bright lights flitted through the air. For a moment I wondered if I was seeing headlights from the roads of the far shore, but no: they moved too fast for that as they swooped and soared, flashing on for a second or two and then blinking off. I admit it: for a moment there I thought I was seeing something very strange indeed. Then I realised. The light from the end of the pier of course shone far into the sky above and around but was quite invisible unless it actually illuminated something - such as the white bellies of seabirds flying in and out of the light.

Another UFO identified. I laughed at myself, dropped the cigarette end into a rain-filled plastic beer-cup in the bin, and walked up to the Lodge.

The following morning I walked to the end of the Craighouse pier, which I hadn't yet done in all my walks and explorations of the locality. The air was chill and fresh, the sun bright, the sea blue. I was amused to see that the "rusty fishing-boat from Ullapool' which Kathleen Jamie mentions in her Jura poem was still there, bobbing at anchor a short way off, with round plastic buoys clustered on its side like grapes, or some monstrous alien roe.

I turned and walked back along the pier, and saw something off to my left that stopped me in my tracks. Behind a stack of pallets on a patch of waste ground by the pier was a pale yellow, stepped, truncated cone with a hatch on its side, atop a short, cylindrical, blackened base.

I picked my way around a fenced-off area and through the weeds and examined it close-up. The hatch had a handle all right, but it wouldn't budge. Though the object was indeed vaguely reminiscent of a space capsule, it was so obviously just a buoy that I found myself blushing and grinning at the same time. Here, surely, was the inspiration for Hamish's story!

I retraced my steps, still smiling, and as I looked at the white buildings of the hotel and distillery and lodge I noticed the phone mast up the hill behind them. It was right in my line of sight. I fished out my Blackberry and peered at it the little mast symbol at the top right of the screen. Predictably but paradoxically, it showed only one tiny bar, barely a square. I shook my head and put the phone away.

Well, I had a science fiction story to write, or at least plan, and no idea at all for one. The sky was clouding over, and I decided to get today's walk in before the rain. I walked around to the other pier, and strolled to the end of the pontoon. On my way back, I noticed on the beach an odd construction: a crude catamaran made from wood and polystyrene, the sort of boat that might be lashed together by people who'd sunk into post-industrial savagery after some catastrophe.

I walked off that pier, past a long tank of whisky on its trailer outside the distillery, then past the Lodge and over the bridge and up the road into the hills. Every now and again I paused to

look out to sea, or to step over to the side of the burn's brown spate. At one point I saw out of the corner of my eye something green and warty in the undergrowth. After a startled moment I looked closer, and saw it was just a weird-looking plant.

The area around the phone mast was fenced off, but the gate was open. I wandered around. I looked closely at the warning sign - which was, rather self-defeatingly, fixed to the shed door. I checked my phone. Still no reception. I shook my head and left, to go back down the hill in a thoughtful mood. The sky darkened by the minute. I sauntered down the hill to the car park and stood by the standing stone, smoking and looking out to sea. A seal swam by, its head leaving a long vee on the smooth, rain-spotted sea. Time to head inside and do some writing. I crossed the road, and crunched up the gravel path to the Lodge.

I didn't have a science fiction story. All I had was cold, hard science fact. If you don't believe me you can look down by the pier yourself. To the best of my knowledge the strange object's still there.

If it isn't, you know why.

MUSIC TO THE MOON AND BACK

Kirsti Wishart

One of the great things about revisiting the Alba ad Astra project is the opportunity it gives to shine a spotlight on other 'lost' areas of Scottish culture. An overlooked star that burns with a fierce, unusual light, is Moira MacKechnie, an unsung heroine of the early Scottish electronic music scene.

I had been entirely unaware of her work until following up references made in the original Alba ad Astra publication to the composer Alexander Turnbull. He'd been commissioned to produce a suitably stirring work for Scotland's exhibit at the 1967 Moscow Expo showcasing the planned space mission that, due to reasons unknown, never took place, the exhibit itself cancelled as a result. As Turnbull's previous work had explored the fringes of electronic composition, he must have been considered a fitting candidate to provide a soundtrack for a display of Scottish pride in technological achievement.

Intrigued by the Turnbull archive referred to in Madeleine Shepherd's investigation into Alba ad Astra, I visited the National Library of Scotland and tracked down the file holding the original score of the Expo piece. I was interested in a note scribbled down the final few pages of the music, 'All Moira's work!', and a red cardboard box that had been brought along to my desk apparently in error, with a paper label on the front saying only, 'MacKechnie's 'Music' '.

It was the quote-marks around 'Music' in particular that drew me and which I was to find typical of Moira MacKechnie's self-deprecating style. Opening the box up, I discovered not only spooled tapes but an old scrapbook filled with newspaper and magazine cuttings on such female pioneers of electronica as Ann Southam, Delia Derbyshire and Daphne Oram. There were also all-too-infrequent references to her own work being played in the Queen's Hall or late night on Radio 3.

One of the compilation tapes found in the box included a recording of 'To the Stars!' Turnbull's Expo piece and the NLS were kind enough to let me listen to it on the equipment they had available. Mid-way through, having reached the section marked as being all Moira's, sitting there in a tiny listening booth, large earphones clamped to my head, I was reminded instantly of the work of Delia Derbyshire in transforming Ron Grainer's composition for the Doctor Who theme tune.

If anything though, Moira's work outmatched Derbyshire's in its otherworldliness. There is the triumphant blast of the orchestra providing the perfect soundtrack to a rocket's take-off, a recording of an actual engine blast also incorporated, the celebration of a Scottish achievement emphasised by the roaring droning from a sixty-seven strong 'bagpipe choir'. Moira's work, however, signifying the moment when the rocket itself is jettisoned, leaving the manned capsule to drift through space is especially striking, spine-tingling in its effectiveness. The music moves from Turnbull's grandiosity into a more abstract, free-floating auditory exploration of weightlessness, the sound reminiscent of Gyrôgi Ligeti's Atmosphères as heard in Kubrick's 2001 but more delicate, fragile and yet with a certain steely, thrawn quality. It sounds like the voices of a flock of space angels who may be offering both a welcome and a warning to these new adventurers. It is alienating, disorientating and profoundly moving, the perfect accompaniment to an altered state; drifting, weightless, seeing Earth in all its glory beneath us, all nationalist sentiment suddenly petty. The fact the space flight, the exhibition and any public performance of Turnbull and MacKechnie's work never took place, added to the yearning, ghostly aspect of the work.

It was then I decided to find out more about Miss MacKechnie and over the years I've been able to piece together her story. Born on Skye in 1940, her obsession with sound developed through being an operator at the manual telephone exchange run by her parents who worked in the Portree Post Office. In a tiny building, little more than a chilly shed next to the Post Office itself, she would transfer calls about the island and became fascinated by the range of the voices and sounds she heard and connected. On quiet days, she would have the opportunity for testing out the new chanter she had recently bought, an interest she maintained throughout her life.

Her delight and skill in the job encouraged her at age 20 to take up the request by a recently widowed elderly aunt to move to Edinburgh to provide companionship. She was able to transfer to one of the city's exchanges but with the transition to automatic exchanges, lost her job only two years later. Fortunately, having joined a Musical Listening Group at Edinburgh Central Library, she made the acquaintance of Alexander Turnbull just at the time when he was looking for a secretary to help catalogue his remarkable outpouring of scores.

Moira appears to have quickly proved herself capable of far more than secretarial work with Turnbull's forays into the electronica shaped by her enthusiasm for the electronic equipment he'd bought largely on a whim. She would take on the roles of sound engineer, composer and experimental musician, making far greater use of the oscillators, tape machines, synthesizers, even a Telharmonium, Turnbull had dotted about his studio. When later asked about her patience with cutting and stitching together loops of tape to produce mesmerising overlays of sound, she referred to the long tradition of knitters and weavers in her family. Studying them, fascinated, meant she developed extraordinary levels of patience, being full aware that delicate, tireless manual labour could result in works of great complexity and beauty.

Although Turnbull alone is referred to as 'composer' on the recordings produced of his electronica, Moira doesn't seem to have begrudged his time in the spotlight. In fact, she may have turned down the opportunity to share greater credit. In clippings of rare interviews in her scrapbook she refers to herself as a 'sound engineer' and seems to have been content to take more of an assistant's role. She plays herself down as an amateur, a hobbyist, seemingly reluctant to take on the pressure of expectation that might come with making a name for herself.

Turnbull himself was well aware of her talent, enough to be instrumental in helping her secure work at the Scottish branch of the Radiophonic Workshop. It seems that she soon grew bored of producing work to meet the BBC's requirements, sound-tracking yet another wildlife documentary, spending hours working on what a centipede would sound or being told off in a memo for making the chittering of bats sound terrifying rather than tuneful. After only five years she left to take a job at the Edinburgh Central Library Music Department, maintaining her sound work as a side interest (I'm sure, in fact, that she was the elderly woman who surprised me by commenting on how much she enjoyed the latest Aphex Twin album I was borrowing as she stamped it, recommending a recently released compilation of 'musique concrète', 'Although it doesn't have quite the same beat to it,' she remarked with a wink).

She became fascinated with ways in which music and sound could be woven into everyday life, convinced that certain vibrations affect us physically. Tuning into the correct frequencies could help heal damaged cells, restore broken connections in the brain. Her flat in Bruntsfield, inherited when her aunt died, was filled with Japanese singing bowls, Tibetan gongs and tuning forks specially calibrated to soothe particular areas of the body along with her ever expanding collection of chanters. She was particularly fond of producing work on the Korg MS-10, an early synthesizer with a 'patch panel' that resembled a telephone switchboard.

You will have heard Moira's work on many an occasion but might not have recognised it as such. In keeping with her character she wanted to design sound to blend into its surroundings but also subconsciously influence the listener. To those in the know, she became known as an acoustic designer who could bring in just the right level of atmospherics in theatre and exhibition design. For the tour of Mary King's Close, she added a layer of sound on the very cusp of hearing in one room – whispered voices, the wind blowing through buildings recently turned desolate – that resulted in many visitors being unable to withstand being in there for more than a minute. Certain traffic lights in Morningside and Bruntsfield have a different tone and beat to the insistent, harping beep we expect to hear in other parts of the city, Moira having arranged those near her to harmonise more closely with the natural rhythms of a pedestrians stride.

I was saddened to discover she died in 2015 but gladdened to find out in an Evening News obituary she received a fitting fanfare; as her coffin was laid to rest, friends, of which there were many, played a Gaelic lament on her collected chanters, each having been left one in her will. I felt her work deserved to be far better known though rather than being limited to a few recordings available in the dustier corners of Youtube. While Moira herself seemed not at all bitter about the lack of recognition she received, looking through her scrapbook, I couldn't help but feel as though hers had been a life lived with the volume turned down. There were a number of half-completed funding applications for projects including an exploration of the acoustic properties of swimming pools, with musical instruments adapted to be played underwater and a tribute to Saint-Saens' 'Carnival of the Animals', involving the squawks, roars, grunts and twitterings of the residents of Edinburgh Zoo recorded and played back to them, creating an animal symphony, visitors encouraged to join in the wild choir, releasing their inner beast. She proposed a composition riffing on the 'stone tape' theory, 'The Singing City' playing with the different frequencies of the granite of Aberdeen, the sandstone of Edinburgh and Glasgow and worked on ways of turning facial expressions into music so that conversations could be accompanied by a constant underlying soundtrack.

I thought of Moira keenly during a recent visit to the Scottish National Gallery of Modern Art when seeing Earth-Moon-Earth, a work by the artist Katie Paterson. Beethoven's Sonata had been translated into Morse Code, transmitted up to the moon and reflected back, the returning message captured full of glitches and absences, notes lost to the Moon's craters. In the gallery space, an automated grand piano played the broken score, eerily unmanned as if a ghost were playing it, its memory fading. The piece seemed to encapsulate Moira's story, giving the breaks and silences resonance, a full work incomplete and yet still beautiful, affecting, quietly dramatic.

Due to the general oddness of the past year, I had difficulty working out if my emotional reaction to the work was due to the weirdness of day-to-day life surrounding it or the art itself. The research I'd been carrying out on Moira had undoubtedly had an effect and as I listened to a composition she'd made combining bird song, wind blowing through the trees on the woods of Raasay and waves of sound from stars recorded by NASA telescopes, I thought of how pleased she'd be to know her music was causing a stranger to experience complicated emotions. I longed for the days when crowds would be able to attend a concert of her work. Perhaps this could be achieved with the realisation of one of her projects, found scribbled on the back of some old sheet music in that red cardboard box in the National Library.

This involved plans for marking the tenth anniversary of the Forth Road Bridge in 1974 by turning it into a massive musical instrument, a transmitter, sending the music she heard in her head all the way up to the stars. She'd taken an interest in the theories of Daphne Oram on archaeological acoustics, suggesting that ancient burial mounds and sites like Stonehenge could be used as resonators. Moira explored similar lines of thought but in relation to modern builds, some of her notes relating to the acoustic potential inherent in fly-overs, multi-storey carparks and pylons. The pared down elegance of the Forth Road Bridge appealed to her far more than the squat heft of the Rail Bridge and she hoped to turn the Bridge into one giant tuning fork, speakers covering its structure, beaming up a choir singing a choral work entitled, 'Tell Them We Are Happy Here', with a force that would cause the Forth to froth. Music journeying to the moon and back with no telling what would come calling after hearing such a summoning. But whatever did, surely it would join us in singing Moira's praises.

Extract from Alexander Turnbull's musical sketch-book. Here we see the composer grappling with his subject, making reference to the great works of the past, such as Mahler's third symphony, and anticipating the avant-garde electronic sounds of Morton Subotnick's Silver Apples of the Moon. While these notes show that Turnbull's sources were international in scope, the piece was destined to have a distinctive Scottish flavour, with the inclusion of a 'bagpipe choir' among the orchestral forces.

Roderick's Letters

Fergus Currie

Dear Kirsti,

I have read your excellent appraisal of Moira MacKechnie's life and work. It brought back lots of special memories of the time. You see, I had the pleasure of knowing Alexander Turnbull during the 1980s while he was working as a part-time professor at Allison House, the music department of Edinburgh University. I am also in the happy position of still having the many of the original tape recordings of his works from that time. My collection is limited to some of the orchestral works and a lot of the electronica. You will be glad to hear that I also have a small number of fragments of Moira's work, which she had entrusted to Alexander for safe keeping since her own home had problems with damp and mould (which would explain her occasional poor health). I heard about the Forth bridge project and my understanding was that she wanted to tune the whole bridge to play a perfect fourth but she was denied permission from the Queensferry council. They had been told by acoustics expert Dr. Murry Campbell that the resulting pitch would be so low that he feared that it would destroy the foundations of the bridge itself. I diverge.

The recordings I have of Moira's work are all short electronica, presumably related to her interest in using sounds of machines and nature in such combinations that they scare the shit out of you! You mentioned her Mary King's tour. I was one of those who survived the whole seven-hour experience. I have scoured the internet for references to both Moira and Alexander in vain. Perhaps your work will spark a renaissance of early Scottish Electronic Music and at long last overturn previous vapid and entirely inaccurate accounts.

I will be delighted to send you digitally remastered versions of all the material I have.

One last thing. I think Turnbull and Moira never actually collaborated on a composition so the margin note 'all Moira's work' probably refers to the transcription of Turnbull's scrawling handwriting rather than the composition. Their style, while superficially related, are clearly established and it would be easy for a good musicologist to determine whether the page in question was in any way a collaboration.

I hope this is useful and I attach one of the mp3s as a token of good faith in your project.

Kindest regards,

Roderick McKracken

Dear Kirsti,

I have tried to contact the archivist at the Alexander Turnbull Foundation but unfortunately failed. Instead, I spoke with his daughter who explained that a serious fire had destroyed almost all of the material relating to Moira MacKechnie. In fact the only extant manuscript of any of her work in the archives is half a page of the Universal Edition of her five and a half hour long *Astral Sacrifice* (1969-70), which was never performed due to the fact that it requires about 200 harpsichords all of which are destroyed during the performance. If Alexander's notes are to be believed, Moira began this work on the occasion of the American Moon landing, apparently incensed by the extravagant budget of the American project compared with the shoe-string financing of the same Scottish programme. You can see on the facsimile page number 322 and a timing of 3 hours 25 minutes and 36 seconds, indicating that the page is from about two thirds of the way through. The score also calls for a Trautonium (a German precursor of the synthesiser invented by Dr. F. Trautwein) and an 'Astral Beacon'. I have no idea what this might have been but it is interesting that on this page at the beginning of the part the notes (the small ones are almost illegible) present the positions of the Jovian moons on the date of the American lunar landing.

I am sorry I cannot be of more help and that the news is not as good as we had hoped but this fragment does give us a tiny glimpse into the mind of this remarkable composer.

Kindest regards,

Roderick McKracken

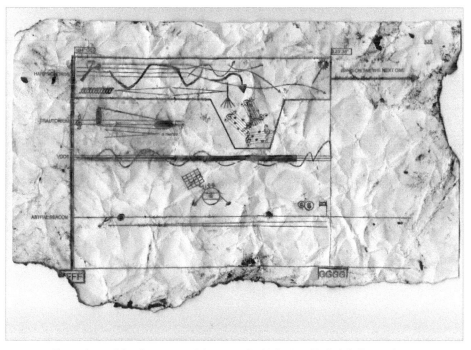

The only surviving fragment of the score for Moira MacKechnie's five and a half hour long Astral Sacrifice (1969-70)

ON THOMAS P. CAMPBELL AND ROCKETRY SCOTLAND

Gavin Inglis

Rocket News

My name is Thomas Camp-
bell and I work
in space as a
rocket man.

ROCKETRY SCOTLAND

Issue One

This is the first issue of the new magazine <u>Rocketry Scotland</u>. It is an answer to those who have said that Scotland should stop invention and exploration while we concentrate on our social problems at home.

Although I am still only a teenager I can see from our history classes that as soon as a country turns its attention inwards it begins to decline. We only have to look at Ancient Greece and Rome and while Scotland is quite different it has made just as much an impact on the world as those XXX civilisations. Perhaps we have forgotten the steam engines of James Watt or the bridges of Thomas Telford. Scots invented the steamship paddle wheel and the screw propellor. Thanks to Alexander Graham Bell's telephone we can talk to people far around the world, and John Logie Baird allows us to see their pictures.

Here in issue one we have a detailed report from your editor's visits to the Empire Exhibition in Bellahouston Park, Glasgow.

The exhibition reminds us of the marvels that we can miss around the world by looking inwards when we should be looking outwards. From the giraffe-necked women to the mechanical man, the speaking clock and of course the Palace of Engineering, the exhibition is a must.

Rocketry is an XXXXXXX exciting field and Scotland needs to take its place. Next issue we will have an article about Professor Goddard and his rocket projects in America. These could all be done here. Remember that the ships built on the Clyde go all the way around the world. The ships of the future will not be restricted to Earth but instead journey round the whole galaxy.

It is easy when walking through Glasgow's gloomy streets in the rain to look only at the ground. But reader, take the trip to Bellahouston Park. You will enter a new world of glass and curves, pass up a street of sparkling fountains, their colours changing all the time. Gather your courage, go to the very top of the Tower of Empire and look out at the magnificent buildings. Look over the whole of Glasgow. Then tell us why should a nation that can achieve all this keep its feet firmly on the ground?

<u>Thomas P. Campbell</u>, September 1938.

Rocketry Scotland

Issue 65   March 1966

EDITORIAL

One of our most popular columns has consistently been <u>Local Launch Pad</u>, reporting the successes of rocketry enthusiasts throughout Scotland and further afield. A particular pleasure of mine is to visit these contributors and witness their efforts first hand.

I recently travelled to a village in the north-east where I met a certain Mr. H. While he has not yet achieved a launch of any significant altitude, we took a light lunch and he told me of an army base in the vicinity. He had witnessed several deliveries by tanker lorries: a quantity of fuel far in excess of that required for the few vehicles parked around the establishment. Mr. H has access to a small rowing boat and after I gained his confidence, confided that he had viewed a concealed area of the base from the seaward side. He swore to me that it contained a free-standing structure and something which looked very much like a rocket.

We attempted to survey the base from the road. I observed a radio tower and several notices which read <u>Ministry of Defence — KEEP OUT</u>. Close to the fence we were intercepted by two kilted members of the Black Watch who warned us off in no uncertain terms. I was sufficiently intrigued to agree to an expedition by boat.

The waters were somewhat choppy and I am not much of a sailor, so I was relieved when Mr H. landed us on a small island barely a half mile from the coast. He led us a rather perilous ascent to a rise from which we could observe a sheltered section of the base.

Although our view was partly obscured, through his field glasses I could make out a red structure which looked very much like a gantry. It reminded me curiously of the Forth Rail Bridge. (Inside this issue you will find a drawing of the ironwork.) At one point a worker in blue overalls passed through my field of vision and I was able to make a comparison. I estimate this gantry to be 50-70 yards in height.

I saw no fuselage or nosecone. However, neither I nor Mr. H could suggest an alternative function for the structure; nor could a mechanical engineer I consulted. I am irresistably forced to speculate that this is the first evidence of the Scottish official rocket programme for which we have been calling all these years.

Rocketry ✹ Scotland

Issue 68   November 1966

Subscribers may be surprised to receive this so close on the heels
of the previous issue. You may also find it somewhat thin. I hope
by the bottom of this page you will understand why this issue has
been so hastily produced, and forgive your editor his unusul state
of agitation. -- TPC.

SCOTLAND'S FIRST MANNED LAUNCH?

Dear Mr. Campbell,
                   I have already written about the increased
security at the M.O.D. base here, and my suspicions that this is a
direct consequence of your report in Rocketry Scotland. The
exclusion zone now covers the island we visited in March and I have
been unable to make any further observations. The access road has
gained a sign marked PRIVATE and a jeep seems permanently stationed
on a nearby hill, day and night. Its occupants are uniformed
soldiers who watch every vehicle which passes.

        We talked before about the intense frustration of being an
informed enthusiast and yet denied access to what may be the single
most important rocketry project on these isles. These last two
weeks have been particularly galling for me because the traffic to
the site has increased, including a number of unmarked civilian
cars. I have felt sure that something was about to happen.

        On Guy Fawkes' Night we mount a small fireworks display at
⟨DELETED⟩ and I took the opportunity to travel there by the base
road. I noticed a glow from the hidden side and stopped the car for
a moment to observe. Upon leaving the area, I hit a deer. They are
common in these parts but tend to avoid lights and noise.

        When I stepped from the car I heard what had startled the
beast: a rumble from the direction of the base, like thunder which
never passed. It grew in volume and even from this distance I felt
the road beneath my feet vibrate. Then I saw it.

        I have imagined a major launch many times. But Mr. Campbell,
nothing prepared me for the strumming against my face, the heat in
my throat, the weakness in my knees. There can be no question of
what lifted from that concealed pad, supported on a perfect
inverted V of fire. Our amateur efforts, our greatest successes --
nothing on Earth can compare to the raw, overbearing power of what

Issue 75

December 1968

EDITORIAL

I must first apologise for the late arrival of this issue. Rocketry Scotland has never kept to a regular schedule, but the delays of the past have been due to want of material rather than editorial ennui.

In this case our contents have been complete for two weeks: Topical Trajectories, Local Launch Pad and The Chart Table were promptly submitted by our regular contributors and up to their usual high standard. However for the first time your editor has been forced to ask himself: why bother?

It is unlikely to surprise the astute regular reader that I have for some time been nurturing contacts within the government; both the Scottish Office and the Ministry of Defence have their rocketry enthusiasts. And while it has never been made official, the overwhelming evidence has pointed to a Scottish space programme, active these last five years. I cannot say by what means the announcement reached me, but I have confirmed it, and can break the news here: this programme has been finally and irrevocably cancelled.

Like myself, you have no doubt been diligently monitoring your wireless and television sets to follow the progress of the Apollo 8 mission, as have the people of every nation. The Americans show us today their audacity, heart and spirit, sending men across the awe-inspiring vacuum of space to orbit the moon.

While here in Scotland, the accountants and bureaucrats wring their hands and shake their heads. As American astronauts become the first to witness Earthrise over the moon, our own government declares a permanent sunset on the age of Scottish exploration. We are to be shopkeepers, plumbers, delivery-men; never again to reach higher.

This may be our last issue. I cannot promise another.

Rocketry 🚀 Scotland

Issue 84   July 1971

I am sorry to break the news that this is the last issue of
Rocketry Scotland. As some of you already know, I have been
fighting a cancer of the throat for over a year. I met with a
specialist and his most optimistic estimate allows six weeks until
the end. I want to put out the final issue now. The condition
leaves me increasingly tired and I am not sure it will be possible
in the weeks to come.

I considered handing the newsletter over to another editor. But
looking back over its thirty-three year run, Rocketry Scotland has
remained a personal project and I think it fitting for it to end
here. Technology is changing and I expect another publication to
appear in its place. As with everything, it is only a matter of
time.

I have been looking over past issues, and the figures for our
circulation. Did you know I hand-typed each copy of issue one? I
barely recognise my own words. Yet fresh memories of the Empire
Exhibition return to me with every day that passes.

What I wrote two and a half years ago was very bitter. While it
remains true, I have moved forward, and our community must too.

We will reach the stars. Fear nothing else. If Scots are not to
take the first steps, we will come close behind; and the first
steps are nothing compared to the adventure that awaits. Remember
when we depart from this world to explore the galaxy, we lose our
nationality, transcend petty strife and become children of Earth on
a frontier whose scale we can barely conceive. It is as natural as
leaving the oceans or taking a first breath.

In departing I must thank all our contributors, and the many
correspondents who offered fascinating insights and carried me
through the hard times. Most of all, I must thank you faithful
readers who kept your postal orders coming year after year. Your
belief was often the only thing which sustained me.

Forgive those who hold us to Earth. They lack only imagination.
It is our duty as rocketeers to lift their eyes to the heavens.

Goodbye.

Thomas P. Campbell.

Eulogy for a Rocketeer

They say everybody needs a hobby. Can you still call it a hobby if it's a lifelong fascination? If it runs through them like their spine? That how it was with my friend Thomas. He was mad for rockets.

We sat together in arithmetic and history. Tom sat by the window. He was always getting in trouble for staring at the sky during lessons. The masters belted him for being inattentive, and I suppose he was. But he was thinking about space.

I'm not sure what got him started with rockets. His father took him to the Empire Exhibition, and after that, all I heard about was one thing or another from the Palace of Engineering. I got so fed up that I said he should start a newsletter about it. It was just my way of telling him to shut up, but the next week Tom came into school and gave me four pages of something called *Rocketry Scotland*. He had typed it all out himself! I suppose it was a limited edition. I just crammed it into my schoolbag. If I'd kept it good it might have been worth a fortune today.

All the optimism of the Exhibition took a knock when the war came. We heard about the Blitz on the wireless. At first it was just London, but then Clydebank. Then Greenock. Although they told us the bombers would only come at night, you had this feeling like you might hear them any time. But you can only stay feart for so long. Once we heard about the V1, and especially the V2, Tom's mother couldn't keep him in the house at night. Other lads went sneaking out to meet girls, dodging the ARP warden for a wee dalliance round the back of the greengrocers. Not Tom. He was up the hill night after night watching the sky for rocket exhaust. You got the feeling that if he met Hitler down the Gallowgate, he would just ask him about the fuel mixture.

Once it was all over Tom got a job in chemical engineering. It was boom time then. I think he hoped it would lead to rockets, but he ended up working with acetylene, on reactors and the new power plants. It was around then he met Annabel and they got married. You know how it is when a man gets responsibilities. He gets used to the steady wage and gives up the schoolboy dreams. But Tom couldn't give it up, not completely. So that was when *Rocketry Scotland* really took off, if you'll forgive the phrase. You can imagine him and Annabel of an evening, her looking for some peace and quiet and him banging away at the typewriter. I think they were happy, although they were only together three or four years before she had the stroke. He never remarried. I don't think he even really looked at another woman.

One thing about magazines you maybe don't know is that when they don't get enough letters, the staff write them under another name. Tom did that in the early days, if you wondered where all these rocket enthusiasts suddenly came from with their controversial opinions. But he never faked the column where he'd visit amateur rocketeers, *Local Launch Pad.* Tom would go anywhere in Scotland if he thought he'd get a launch and a sandwich out of it. From Stranraer to Stromness, he just got in his motor and went. Slept on a couch or drove through the night.

Those were his weekends, and he was never happier.

If you followed the magazine, you heard about what was supposedly an official rocket programme that was cancelled. There have been suggestions that Tom was working as an engineer on the project, and he had to keep it quiet because of the Official Secrets Act. I don't know. I don't think that was true. He wouldn't have told me directly, but the idea that he could have kept it secret – that he could have contained his excitement – seems preposterous. I feel sure there would have been something: a wee smile, a raised eyebrow, silence instead of an obvious reply. All I know is, he kept writing the magazine and sending it out. Could he have been playing both sides? I don't know.

We had plans for the biggest boys' night out you've ever heard of – going to America for the launch of Apollo 13. Tom knew somebody in Florida that would put us up. But that was when he started to get sick, and we had to cancel. I went to visit him instead, and we watched *Star Trek* on the television. He couldn't really talk, but he wrote on a pad. He liked that the chief engineer was a Scotsman. I think he put out two more issues of *Rocketry Scotland* before he passed.

I didn't see him in his last weeks, but I talked to a nurse who was there. She said that sometimes dying people reach a point of acceptance, and a peace comes over them. Grace, she called it. Tom got her to push his bed against the window, and he wouldn't draw the curtains at night. She found him one morning with his eyes wide open, staring into the sun. But the doctor said he'd been dead for five or six hours. You know he was looking at the stars.

Coda to the Last Man in Space:

Transcript of an audio file

discovered on Madeleine

Shepherd's abandoned laptop

March 2021

The funny thing about well-wishers is that things never turn out as well as they wished. This was certainly true of the well-wisher who dumped the Scottish Office memos on Hector MacKraken, and it's true of the one who sent me a bunch of yellowing photographs about 10 years later.

Back in 2009 I did try to find Hector again but failed. It seemed he'd already got wind of the potential crash landing, and gone off to track it down. Having fallen out with him over his book and my exhibition, I didn't put much effort into pursuing him.

The mainstream media didn't report the space junk re-entry.

Amateur astronomy networks were awash with photos of the St Andrew's Day fireball, though – it was assumed to have been completely incinerated. This was enough of a coincidence to prompt me to email Roberta in Australia for any more information she might have. It was Roberta who tipped me off about the signals in the first place. As it turned out, she'd been abruptly redeployed well away from tracking space junk, and was very reluctant to discuss the matter. While her reticence felt odd, I didn't want to make things awkward so I changed the subject to possums. I hear she's now switched careers to wildlife rescue... Damn those possums!

Life did its usual thing of carrying on, distracting me with work and family for a couple of years. I can't say I'd completely forgotten about Hector and his missing father, but it certainly wasn't uppermost in my mind when I bumped into Andrew in a pub – where else? He told me about a chance encounter he'd had a few weeks earlier. Andrew and some writer friends had met a rather arch ex-civil servant. I think his name was Hugh something. He'd muscled in on the conversation to wheedle drinks out of the group in exchange for some tall tale about Scots in space.

Ordinarily, this would have been dismissed as exactly that but Andrew knew about my investigation with Hector. Too many of the details matched up to just ignore it. I figured the guy had read Hector's book or seen my exhibition and was having a laugh at their expense. He'd probably made up the bit about a crash landing On Barra for "authenticity" but it stayed with me. What if something had come back, after all? What if Hector's dad had survived? What if I didn't take my next assignment and couldn't pay the rent?

I decided to be grown up and take the work, but I did contact the other folk who'd been part of my investigation back in 2009. It seemed that some of them couldn't quite leave the idea of Scotland's forgotten space endeavours alone either. We found different routes through the web of hints and documents to our own nuggets of historical gold. My discoveries concerned Hector's father, Bill MacKraken, and all sorts of exploits – exploring the Amazon jungle, playing "Zen bebop" with Charlie Parker, coral diving in the South Seas. His timeline really didn't add up, and I was beginning to wonder if he had doppelgängers or was some kind of immortal. Kirsti brought me back to reality with the story of Moira MacKechnie, a pioneering composer who'd been inspired by the potential of Scottish space exploration. Gav was deep into researching the amateur rocketeers of mid-twentieth-century Scotland. I was pleased that it wasn't all government cover-ups. Then I heard back from Ken.

Ken had been with Andrew on the night of the tall tale but he'd left pretty soon after for a writer's retreat on Jura. He didn't get my message until he got back. Ken set off with Hugh's stories in mind and, brought back an eye-witness account of a splash down. He had some pictures. The photos were partly intended to debunk the account, but they also gave it some substance. So here I was back in the land of paranoia and alternative reality. And I had those questions again. What if something had come back, after all? What if Hector's dad had survived? It seemed a bit more likely now. Was it Barra or Jura? Jura is nice at that time of year. There must be some wildlife I could photograph. Golden eagles maybe – no, wait, that was the name of MacKraken's rocket. What about porpoises? Yes, I'd get a fishing boat to take me out to see the porpoises.

Once on Jura it was easy to find the hotel bar where Ken had met his witness, Hamish the fisherman. Indeed, it was easy to find the man himself. He told me the same tale and more.

Apparently, not long after the incident with the capsule, a very agitated man arrived asking questions. He was trying to find his long-lost father, and had Hector's wiry grey hair and long, sallow face, so I'm fairly certain it was him. He wanted to go out to sea right away. Everyone in the harbour knew it was a bad day for a voyage, but Hector was insistent. The description of his stomping off to find a boat for himself was also all too recognisable. Not long afterwards, a bunch of planks lashed onto anything that might float was spotted up the coast by a friend of Hamish. It was too far out to be see clearly in the rain, but they figured it was probably paddled by Hector. They never saw him again and, until I arrived, no one came looking for him.

With the weather improving and some financial encouragement, Hamish agreed to take me out to photograph porpoises via the site of the splash down he'd reported to Ken. There was nothing to see at the site, but I had an eerie feeling as Hamish told me what he had seen. A lot of it fitted so well. Still, it was not hard to keep a grip on my scepticism and assess the whole story – a warty, green alien who could paddle a raft, indeed! No doubt Hamish thought he was giving us city folk what we'd paid for.

Further out we found a lovely school of porpoises feeding and playing around the Corryvreckan whirlpool. Between Jura and Scarba, the narrow strait and the shape of the sea floor create ideal conditions for a massive whirlpool. "Third largest in the world", Hamish told me as he steered his little craft around the standing waves. "This is a good day, but your man set out on his raft in a raging westerly. He's likely down there now. Except he wouldn't actually stay down with these currents." Hamish pointed at the centre of the foaming, whirling water.

As I continued to grab images of the delightful porpoises as they broke the surface into the sunshine, my thoughts turned a little darker. If it really had been Hector MacKraken on the raft, then perhaps the fabled kraken had reclaimed one of its wayward sons. But what of his father, Bill MacKraken? Was it his return that Hamish witnessed? He could tell me nothing about the helicopter but its general direction of travel towards the mainland. *Nothing more to find out in the islands*, I thought. The doings of outsiders are an amusing distraction, and they get on with the task at hand as the novelty evaporates.

At home, I took stock of all the bits and pieces. I didn't resort to plastering a wall with notes and pictures and connecting them with red string, but I might has well have done. It all happened in my head – tenuous connections between photographs, tangential documentation, hearsay, hints and tall tales told by strange men with names beginning with H. If I thought that was significant, I really needed to step back for a while.

It seemed that Hector may well have been lost at sea, but there were a couple of loose ends dangling – his parents. Very little had come to light about Mrs MacKraken. What's more, her husband, Bill, if Hamish was to be believed, was last seen literally dangling from a helicopter over the sea off Jura. I had almost no success tracking down details of the MacKraken family, even allowing for alternative spellings of their surname.

From a copy of Hector's birth records, I got first and maiden names for his mother, Magda Kowalska. There was no marriage certificate, and no older documentation for either of them. I supposed Magda might have been a stateless orphan after the Second World War, but Bill should surely be somewhere in the National Records of Scotland.

I remembered his puzzling timeline from my library research. He seemed to have had too many adventures for one lifetime.

Then he disappeared while his son was an infant, and his son vanished as he returned from another adventure. If this was all one person, making mischief and living forever, it would explain the lack of documents. Of course, you'd have to believe in immortality for that to work, and even then, the dates don't quite add up. I had to rein in my imagination. This would be fine in a story where you can make up the rules, but not in real life.

Everything went back in a box marked "do not open" until 2020, the year of pandemic and lockdown. It was the year when we finally realised who held the world together – medics, delivery drivers, carers, supermarket staff. The rest of us were kept indoors out of reach of the virus. I was on team indoors, brooding about the future and the past. I guess I wasn't the only one because this was when our second well-wisher popped up.

A small envelope arrived in the post one morning thank you, lockdown posties! – addressed in an unknown hand. It contained four fading black-and-white photographs of a construction site showing a domed structure, and the assembly of an upturned cone with a cylinder above. The small human figures in two of the pictures gave a sense of the size of the build. Whatever it was, it would be big enough inside for three men to live for a few days. Between the pictures was a note in the same handwriting. It read:

"To find what you seek, show these to Will McKay at The Birches Nursing Home, Barnton, Edinburgh. Sent by a well-wisher."

I was all over the images with a magnifying glass, but there was nothing to give away the location or the identity of the figures.

I started turning over the name in my head. Will McKay – William McKay – William MacKay – William MacK. ...William MacKraken! It had to be Bill, didn't it? Why else would I be sent these photos to show him? But he was in a nursing home. I'd seen my share of elderly relatives fade away, and it sounded like he might be in the same state. The shock of a strange visitor asking about his past might be too much for him. On the other hand, the chance to tell his story to someone who didn't dismiss it might be just what he needed.

I phoned The Birches to arrange a visit. Of course, it was impossible. Not even close family are allowed to see nursing home residents during a pandemic. I sent Will McKay a card by way of making contact but I didn't send copies of the photos. I need to see his immediate reaction for myself.

It's now February 2021 and the infection risks are decreasing. Until today, I was still hopeful of a visit after the restrictions are finally eased. Will is apparently quite fit for a man in his eighties, but his dementia is getting worse. He keeps asking the staff about his warty, green pal, and ranting about what the world owes him for 40 unplanned years of space travel. That would certainly sound demented to the uninitiated. But today I got several phone calls, from The Birches and from the police.

Will's bed was found empty, the window open and his nightly medication had been spat out into a saucer. As the only person taking an interest in him, The Birches have asked me to contact them if he turns up at my house. I suspect he might but I'm not sure I'd recognise the next version of the shape-shifting Mr MacKraken.

[Editor's Note: The recording ends with the sound of a door bell, the shuffling of papers, and some muttering about supermarket deliveries.]

The desk of Madeleine Shepherd.

This picture shows the table and its contents just as she left these before her disappearance. The items on the desktop consist of research materials relating to the Alba ad Astra project. The four black-and-white photographs of an unidentified construction project, which she had received only days earlier, are laid out on the laptop computer in the upper left of the picture. An unsaved Word file was open on the laptop (not shown). This took the form of a twenty-seven-word quatrain, which appears to be a pastiche or parody of *Antagonish* by William Hughes Mearns:

> *Last night, I had to stop and stare*
> *At someone who was not quite there...*
> *I saw that man again today,*
> *And now he's stolen me away!*

Contributors

Fergus Currie is a double bass player in the Greek National Opera. He is also a composer, origami designer, author, Takemitsu scholar, captain of the Papagou Veterans chess team, Tai-Chi expert, poet, librettist, jazz arranger, model airplane designer and amateur chef. In his spare time, he solves crossword puzzles and makes animation videos of his cat Ernesto. He lives in Greece with his wife Maria.

https://soundcloud.com/fergus-currie

Andrew C Ferguson has had poetry, short stories and book length projects published in various places over the years. These include *The Wrong Box*, a comic crime novel set in Edinburgh (Thunderpoint, 2017). He is currently focusing on songwriting and playing in bands: his solo output is at https://andrewfergusonassiasa.bandcamp.com/ He will soon live in Edinburgh.

Pippa Goldschmidt is a fiction and essay writer. She used to work in space policy for the UK Government and she likes writing about science. Her latest project was co-editing (with Dr Gill Haddow and Dr Fadhila Mazanderani) *Uncanny Bodies*, an academic-creative anthology inspired by Freud, cities and cyborgs, published by Luna Press. Please visit at www.pippagoldschmidt.co.uk and @goldipipschmidt

Gavin Inglis works primarily in games, with interactive novels published through Choice of Games and credits on *Zombies, Run!, Call of Cthulhu,* and *Fallen London*. He was Language and Cognition Fellow at the Department for Clinical Neuroscience, during which he produced a graphic novel about Functional Neurological Disorder, and AI versions of Jane Austen and H.P. Lovecraft. www.gavininglis.com.

Ken MacLeod was born on the Isle of Lewis and lives in Gourock. He is the author of seventeen novels, from *The Star Fraction* (1995) to *The Corporation Wars* (2018), and many articles and short stories. He is currently writing a space opera trilogy.
http://kenmacleod.blogspot.com @amendlocke

Madeleine Shepherd is an interdisciplinary artist with an interest in science, maths and science fiction. Her work ranges from collaborative projects like the one you're reading to hand-crafted fashion accessories. Notable pieces include collaborative installation Botanica Mathematica and community art work Knit the Shoreline. She is currently working on mathematically-inspired knitwear and wall hangings of the early space race.
www.madeleineshepherd.co.uk

Andrew J. Wilson's short stories, non-fiction and poems have appeared all over the world, sometimes in the most unlikely places. With Neil Williamson, he co-edited *Nova Scotia: New Scottish Speculative Fiction*, which was nominated for a World Fantasy Award. Andrew was also put forward for the 2020 Dwarf Stars Award.
www.andrewjwilsonpublishingservices.co.uk

Kirsti Wishart's stories have appeared in *New Writing Scotland, 404 Ink Magazine, Product*, and *Biopolis: Tales of Urban Biology.* Her first novel, *The Knitting Station*, was published by Rymour Books in March 2021. She is working on a book about Scottish psychogeography and loves a good wander. Say hello @kirstiw

Artist's Statement

Collaborative space by
Madeleine Shepherd

Chancelot Mill was the start of it all. I've been photographing it on and off for years in different lights and always wondered why it looked quite so dramatic. As a child of the "white heat of technology" I've always been interested in Scotland's scientific and technological heritage. Looking at the Mill and other images of derelict industrial sites it occurred to me that, if things had been different in the sixties, we might have had a Scottish Space programme. The name Alba ad Astra immediately sprang to mind.

Back in 2008, I'd been following the work of artists Aleksandra Mir and Eames Demetrios and thought a portfolio of these photographs, suitably annotated, would fit into the tradition of alternate geographies and space-travel-inspired works which they, and others, were establishing. A lot of my previous work had been based on taking objects out of their normal context and applying new roles to them. The Alba ad Astra photographs and captions fulfil this by asking the viewer to question the reality they appear to represent.

Rather than write captions myself, I approached my friends in Writers' Bloc with the idea that they could contribute the captions. They took the idea to heart and carried it further than I thought possible. It was important to me that the images remain untouched but there was complete freedom to work round them. It is left as an exercise for the reader to distinguish the things we made up and the things we didn't have to invent. I also approached my brother, Fergus Currie, the originator of the Bill MacKraken character, who seemed to be the ideal protagonist for this enterprise. Fergus' enthusiastic response kick-started my writing and his ideas are incorporated throughout the project.

The 2009 exhibition was complemented by a 44 page booklet of stories, documents and images, which I came to feel was incomplete. Not all of the Rocketry Scotland documents in the exhibition were prepared in time for the publication. In the intervening years, Andrew J. Wilson and Ken MacLeod both wrote new stories using the Alba ad Astra idea. I continued taking photographs. The opportunity to bring the existing pieces together and write new work presented itself in 2020 during the Covid 19 lockdown when *Shoreline of Infinity* agreed to publish this new volume. Revisiting the work gave us the impetus to create new pieces and to tie up a few loose ends. What we have now is a truly collaborative piece with interwoven stories and artefacts. In the process a new loose end unravelled itself. So, the door is open for more adventures with Bill MacKraken if any of us dare to step over the threshold.

April 2021

(updated from the 2009 version)

Acknowledgements

Alba ad Astra was always a communal work. It would never have existed without the enthusiasm, support and effort of the 2009 team. Thank you to my fellow Alba ad Astronauts, Gavin, Andrew, Kirsti, Fergus and Andrew.

Thanks are also due to Ken MacLeod and Pippa Goldschmidt for their support and for writing such appropriate forewords and to Carmen Moran for her mission patch design.

I greatly appreciate Noel Chidwick's editorial and layout work as well as his ongoing enthusiasm for my project.

Finally, a very special thank you must go to Mike Calder of Transreal Fiction Bookshop for hosting the original 2009 exhibition, financing this new volume and for his long term moral support of this artist.

Madeleine Shepherd

April 2021

Shoreline of Infinity

...is based in Edinburgh, Scotland, and began life in 2015.

Shoreline of Infinity Science Fiction Magazine is a digital magazine published monthly in PDF, ePub and Kindle formats. It features new short stories, poetry, art, reviews and articles.

We are open for submissions from new and established writers – details of our regular submission windows are available on our website.

But there's more – we run regular live science fiction events called Event Horizon, with a whole mix of science fiction related entertainments such as story and poetry readings, author talks, music, drama, short films – we've even had sword fighting. Event Horizon is mostly monthly, and before covid-19 we hosted them live, in a real venue, with people mingling – hard to imagine, eh? We're online now, of course, but that does mean you can join in from anywhere in the world.

When we return to venue events, we will continue to livestream them, though. For details, visit the website.

We also publish a range of science fiction linked books, take a look at our collection at the Shoreline Shop. You can also pick up back copies of all of our issues, thanks to the wonders of digital publishing and print on demand. Details on our...

www.shorelineofinfinity.com